Raintree Steck-Vaughn

Illustrated
SCIENCE
ENCYCLOPEDIA

Volume
2

ANT – BEE

RSVP

**RAINTREE
STECK-VAUGHN**
P U B L I S H E R S
The Steck-Vaughn Company

Austin, Texas

Published by Raintree Steck-Vaughn Publishers, an imprint of
Steck-Vaughn Company.

Executive Editor	Diane Sharpe
Senior Editor	Anne Souby
Design Manager	Joyce Spicer

This edition edited and designed by Andromeda Oxford Ltd.

Andromeda Editorial and Design

Project Manager	Julia Roles
Editorial Manager	Jenny Fry
Design	TT Designs, T&S Truscott
Cover Design	John Barker

Library of Congress Cataloging-in-Publication Data
Raintree Steck-Vaughn illustrated science encyclopedia.
       p.   cm.
    Includes bibliographical references and index.
    Summary: A twenty-four volume set containing brief articles
on science topics.
    ISBN 0-8172-3943-X (set)
    ISBN 0-8172-3920-0 (Volume 2)
    1. Science—Encyclopedias, Juvenile. [1. Science—
Encyclopedias.]   I. Raintree Steck-Vaughn Publishers.
Q121.R354   1997
503—dc20   96-11078
                                            CIP
                                            AC

Printed and Bound in the United States of America.
1 2 3 4 5 6 7 8 9 10 IP 00 99 98 97 96

Using the Raintree Steck-Vaughn Illustrated Science Encyclopedia

You are living in a world in which science, technology, and nature are very important. You see something about science almost every day. It might be on television, in the newspaper, in a book at school, or some other place. Often, you want more information about what you see.

The *Raintree Steck-Vaughn Illustrated Science Encyclopedia* will help you find what you want to know. It contains information on many science subjects. You may want to find out about computers, the environment, space exploration, biology, agriculture, or mathematics, for example. They are all in the *Raintree Steck-Vaughn Illustrated Science Encyclopedia.* There are many, many other subjects covered as well.

There are twenty-four volumes in the encyclopedia. The articles, which are called entries, are in alphabetical order through the first twenty-two volumes. On the spine of each volume, below the volume number, are some letters. The letters above the line are the first three letters of the first entry in that volume. The letters below the line are the first three letters of the last entry in that volume. In Volume 1, for example, you see that the first entry begins with **AAR** and that the last entry begins with **ANT**. Using the letters makes it easy to find the volume you need.

In Volume 23, there are three special features—reference charts and tables, a bibliography, and an index. In Volume 24, there are interesting projects that you can do on your own. The projects are fun to do, and they help you discover and understand important science principles. Many can give you ideas that can help you develop your own science fair projects.

Main Entries There are two kinds of main entries in the *Raintree Steck-Vaughn Illustrated Science Encyclopedia.* Many of the entries are major topics that are spread over several pages. The titles of these entries are shown at the top of the page in a yellow box. Other entries required less space to cover the topic fully. The titles of these main entries are printed in capital letters. They look like this: **ABALONE**. At the beginning of some entries, you will see a phonetic pronunciation of the entry title, such as (ăb′ ə lō′ nē).

In the front of each volume, there is a pronunciation key. Use it the same way you use your dictionary's pronunciation key.

Cross-References Within the main entries are cross-references referring to other entries in the encyclopedia. Within an entry, they look like this: (see MAMMAL). At the end of an entry, they look like this: *See also* HYENA. These cross-references tell you where to find other helpful information on the subject you are reading about.

Projects At the end of some entries, you will see this symbol: PROJECT 1. It tells you which projects related to that entry are in Volume 24.

Illustrations There are thousands of photographs, drawings, graphs, diagrams, tables, and other illustrations in the *Raintree Steck-Vaughn Illustrated Science Encyclopedia.* They will help you better understand the entries you read. Captions describe the illustrations. Many of the illustrations also have labels that point out important parts.

Activities Some main entries include activities presented in a special box. These activities are short projects that give you a chance to work with science on your own.

Index In Volume 23, the index lists every main entry by volume and page number. Many subjects that are not main entries are also listed in the index, as well as the illustrations, projects, activities, and reference charts and tables.

Bibliography In Volume 23, there is also a bibliography for students. The books in this list are on a variety of topics and can supplement what you have learned in the *Raintree Steck-Vaughn Illustrated Science Encyclopedia.*

The *Raintree Steck-Vaughn Illustrated Science Encyclopedia* was designed especially for you, the student. It is a source of knowledge for the world of science, technology, and nature. Enjoy it!

PRONUNCIATION KEY

Each symbol has the same sound as the darker letters in the sample words.

ə	balloon, ago	îr	deer, pier	r	root, tire
ă	map, have	j	join, germ	s	so, press
ā	day, made	k	king, ask	sh	shoot, machine
âr	care, bear	l	let, cool	t	to, stand
ä	father, car	m	man, same	th	thin, death
b	ball, rib	n	no, turn	*th*	then, this
ch	choose, nature	ng	bring, long	ŭ	up, cut
d	did, add	ŏ	odd, pot	ûr	urge, hurt
ĕ	bell, get	ō	cone, know	v	view, give
ē	sweet, easy	ô	all, saw	w	wood, glowing
f	fan, soft	oi	boy, boil	y	yes, year
g	good, big	ou	now, loud	z	zero, raise
h	hurt, ahead	o͝o	good, took	zh	leisure, vision
ĭ	rip, ill	o͞o	boot, noon	'	strong accent
ī	side, sky	p	part, scrap	'	weak accent

GUIDE TO MEASUREMENT ABBREVIATIONS

All measurements in the *Raintree Steck-Vaughn Illustrated Science Encyclopedia* are given in both the customary system and the metric system [in brackets like these]. Following are the abbreviations used for various units of measure.

Customary Units of Measure

mi. = miles	cu. yd. = cubic yards
m.p.h. = miles per hour	cu. ft. = cubic feet
yd. = yards	cu. in. = cubic inches
ft. = feet	gal. = gallons
in. = inches	pt. = pints
sq. mi. = square miles	qt. = quarts
sq. yd. = square yards	lb. = pounds
sq. ft. = square feet	oz. = ounces
sq. in. = square inches	fl. oz. = fluid ounces
cu. mi. = cubic miles	°F = degrees Fahrenheit

Metric Units of Measure

km = kilometers	cu. km = cubic kilometers
kph = kilometers per hour	cu. m = cubic meters
m = meters	cu. cm = cubic centimeters
cm = centimeters	ml = milliliters
mm = millimeters	kg = kilograms
sq. km = square kilometers	g = grams
sq. m = square meters	mg = milligrams
sq. cm = square centimeters	°C = degrees Celsius

For information on how to convert customary measurements to metric measurements, see the Metric Conversions table in Volume 23.

ANTENNAE Antennae are sense organs of insects and other arthropods (see ARTHROPODA). Pairs of antennae project from the animals' heads and are used mainly for touching, smelling, or hearing. Tiny hairlike nerves in the antennae pick up sensations.

Ants use their antennae to follow a scent. The silk moth can use its antennae to smell another silk moth that may be up to 6 mi. [10 km] away. Insects that live in darkness often use their antennae to avoid bumping into things. Some small crustaceans use their antennae to move themselves through water.

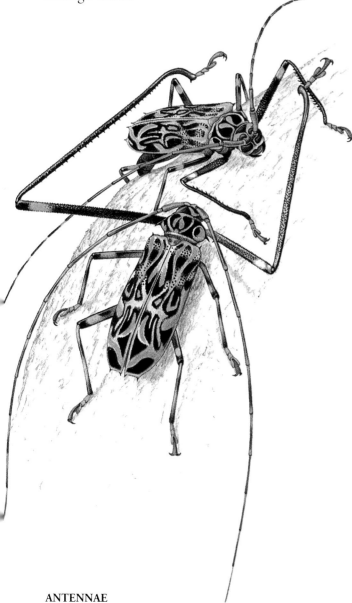

ANTENNAE

Arthropods, such as these harlequin beetles, sense their environment with their antennae. Tiny hairs growing from arthropods' antennae are sensitive to such things as taste, touch, movement, and smell.

ANTHER

Anthers, shown here in a tulip, are the pollen-producing parts of flowering plants. They are located at the ends of the filaments. The anthers and filaments together make up the stamens, or male parts, of flowers.

ANTHER An anther is part of the stamen (male part) of a flower (see STAMEN). The anther contains the pollen, which is used in reproduction. The anther is connected to the flower by a slender stalk, called a filament. Anthers usually have four swollen parts containing pollen. When the pollen is ripe, the swollen parts of the anther break open. This releases the pollen. Some anthers open with a small explosion. The explosion blows the pollen into the air. Otherwise, the pollen stays on the anther. In either case, the wind may then blow the pollen away. Sometimes pollen from the anther sticks to the hairs of insects or to the beaks of birds. They may then carry it to other flowers. *See also* POLLINATION.

ACTIVITY *How to see pollen*

Take a buttercup or a poppy flower and tap it sharply to knock some pollen onto a sheet of plain paper. Use a strong magnifying glass to look closely at the pollen. Most pollen has an irregular surface which helps it stick to insects during pollination.

ANTHERIDIUM (ăn′thə rĭd′ē əm) An antheridium is the male sex organ found on the sexual generation (the gametophyte) of ferns, mosses, hornworts, liverworts, and some species of algae and fungi.

See also ALTERNATION OF GENERATIONS; ARCHEGONIUM.

ANTHROPOID

The rhesus monkey is an example of an anthropoid ape. It lives in the foothills of the Himalayas, from Afghanistan to China.

ANTHROPOID

An anthropoid is a highly developed mammal that is also a primate (see PRIMATE). Anthropoids form one of the two major groups of primates. Humans, the apes, and the monkeys belong to the anthropoids. Other primates, such as lemurs and tarsiers, are included in the other group called the prosimians.

An anthropoid has a flattened face with eyes in the front of the skull. Its brain is relatively large in proportion to its body. An anthropoid has stereoscopic vision, which allows it to judge distance.

ANTHROPOLOGY

Anthropology is the study of humankind. It deals with the way humans lived in the past and the way humans live today. It began as a science in the 1800s. Anthropology is an outgrowth of biology and the social sciences. It has two main divisions: physical anthropology and cultural anthropology.

Physical anthropology deals with the origin and development of the human species from a biological standpoint. It studies the skeletons of humans to learn how humans evolved and how we have changed. It also studies the differences between human beings who live in different places. The colors of hair and skin, the shapes of heads and bodies, and the different types of human blood are some of the things physical anthropologists study and compare.

Cultural anthropology deals with how and why humans behave as they do. Cultural anthropologists note such things as family and large-group structure. They study a society's customs, work habits, recreational pursuits, language, visual arts, crafts, music, and literature. They also study the medicine, religion, and technology of particular societies.

Louis Leakey, a Kenyan of British descent, and Margaret Mead of the United States are two famous anthropologists (see LEAKEY FAMILY; MEAD, MARGARET). Leakey, a physical anthropologist, devoted most of his life to searching for the fossil remains of prehistoric humans. He discovered, in Africa, the skulls of humanlike creatures who lived millions of years ago. Margaret Mead, a cultural anthropologist, studied people who lived without a written language or machines. She spent many years in the islands of the South Pacific.

See also ARCHEOLOGY; EVOLUTION; FOSSIL; HUMAN BEING.

ANTIBIOTIC

Antibiotics are chemical substances that microorganisms produce to protect themselves against harm from other living organisms. People generally use antibiotics to control disease. The first antibiotic discovered was penicillin. In 1928, Alexander Fleming, a British scientist, found that a chemical secreted by a mold called *Penicillium notatum* had stopped the growth of bacteria in a laboratory culture. He named the antibiotic after the mold (see BACTERIA; FLEMING, SIR ALEXANDER; PENICILLIN).

Antibiotics work by several different means. Some antibiotics, such as penicillin, interfere with the ability of bacteria to make cell walls. This prevents these bacteria from growing and reproducing. Other antibiotics interfere with bacteria's ability to make proteins. If a bacterium cannot make proteins, it dies. Antibiotics that prevent bacteria from multiplying are called bacteriostatic, while those that kill bacteria are called bacteriocidal.

Sometimes, through genetic means, bacteria can produce offspring bacteria that are not affected by an antibiotic. These new bacteria are said to be resistant to the antibiotic.

In 1957, the chemical structure of penicillin was discovered. By making changes in that structure, scientists were able to make new varieties of the antibiotic. Bacteria that had become resistant to the original drug could be controlled successfully with one of the new varieties of penicillin.

In the 1940s, Selman Waksman, a Russian-American biologist, tested various organisms to find those that would produce antibiotics. As a result of his research, actinomycin, streptomycin, the tetracyclines, and other antibiotics were found (see WAKSMAN, SELMAN ABRAHAM). Penicillin, streptomycin, and the tetracyclines are called broad-spectrum antibiotics because they are effective in the treatment of many different kinds of infections. Some antibiotics are used only against particular diseases or microorganisms. These are called narrow-spectrum antibiotics. Actinomycin, for example, is used to prevent the growth of some cancers.

Antibiotics make up the most powerful group of drugs we have for controlling infectious disease. They are used most successfully against diseases caused by bacteria and rickettsiae, many of which were once extremely dangerous to people (see RICKETTSIA). It is because of the use of antibiotics that serious infectious diseases such as tuberculosis, dysentery, syphilis, and typhus can be controlled.

Sometimes antibiotics are used to prevent infection. They are usually given to a patient before he or she has surgery in which a foreign object, such as a metal kneecap, is to be left in the body.

Some antibiotics are fed to healthy poultry and livestock to make them grow faster and to keep them healthy. Using antibiotics in the food of healthy animals means that many bacteria are allowed to build up a resistance to them. This means that the antibiotics will be less effective against disease. Almost half the antibiotics produced in the United States are used in this way. In some other countries, giving antibiotics to healthy animals is no longer legal.

Thousands of antibiotics have been developed, and nearly one hundred of those are used by doctors to treat various diseases in humans. Some are designed by chemists and then made synthetically (artificially).

Among the recently developed antibiotics are amphotericine B, nystatin, ampicillin, the cephalosporins, and vidarabine. The first two are used to treat fungus infections. Ampicillin is used against intestinal infections, among others. The cephalosporins are a group of synthetically made antibiotics and are an alternative for people who are allergic to penicillin. Vidarabine is the only antibiotic known to destroy viruses. It is used to treat certain eye infections and to combat the disease shingles.

See also MICROORGANISM.

ANTIBODY (ăn′tĭ bŏd′ē) An antibody is a protein made by a body's immune system. Antibody production is caused by the presence of antigens. Antigens are proteins or carbohydrates, but they do not normally belong in the body. These foreign substances are found in bacteria, viruses, insects, snake venom, and transplanted organs from another person (see TRANSPLANTATION). Both the antigens and the antibodies circulate in the blood.

Each antibody is made by the immune system to fight a particular kind of antigen. The antibodies that destroy one antigen will not usually affect another one. Antigens are destroyed because the antibodies bind closely with them. This binding of antigen to antibody is a signal for immune system cells to attack the antigen.

Once a certain kind of antigen has been destroyed, the body may have the ability to quickly produce more antibodies to fight a second attack, if needed. If this happens, the body has become immune to that antigen (see IMMUNITY). If the antigen is part of a disease-causing organism, the person probably will not get the disease again. This is the principle behind vaccination, in which antigens that are too weak to produce actual disease are injected into the body. The body starts producing antibodies, which quickly destroy the antigens. The body then has the ability to quickly make more of these antibodies, and so the person does not normally get the disease if exposed to it at a later time. Vaccinations have controlled the spread of many diseases, such as tuberculosis, polio, and measles (see DISEASE; PATHOGEN; VACCINATION).

Some antigens are poisons called toxins. Antibodies that neutralize these toxins are called antitoxins (see ANTITOXIN). For example, poisonous snakes have a strong toxin that they release through their fangs when they bite. The body of the bitten person starts to produce antitoxins to fight this poison. In some cases, the poison may be so strong that the body cannot produce enough antitoxins quickly enough to fight the poison. Artificial antitoxins must be injected, or the person may die.

ANTICLINE An anticline is a bending in layers of rock that make up the earth's crust. It is also called an upfold, which is a formation that looks like an upside-down U. An anticline is caused when rock is squeezed by sideways (horizontal) forces from opposite directions. These forces, or pressures, push the rock upward (see FOLDING; STRATIFICATION).

Some anticlines contain rock that is folded up and down. An anticline with upfolds and down-folds is called an anticlinorium. An anticlinorium has one major upfold. It also has minor upfolds and downfolds.

An anticline is most often identified by the crest, or top, of the fold. Geologists also identify anticlines by comparing rock on opposite sides of the crest. If the rock on both sides is the same, usually the structure is an anticline.

Geologists used to think that anticlines were the most important sign of underground oil and natural gas. In the 1930s, geologists began to realize that anticlines are not the only important signs of such deposits.

See also GEOLOGY; SYNCLINE.

ANTICLINE

Pictured above is a typical anticline, or, as it is sometimes called, an upfold. Anticlines are caused by forces coming from opposite directions. These forces push the rock layers upward.

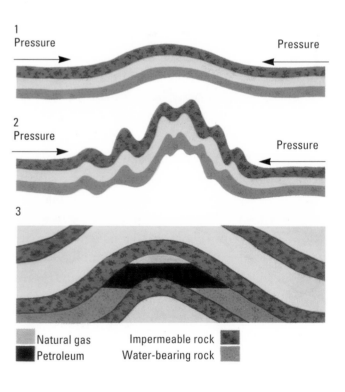

Natural gas   Impermeable rock
Petroleum   Water-bearing rock

Stages in the formation of an anticline: (1) Pressure forms a simple anticline; (2) a complex anticline, or anticlinorium, forms; (3) the crest of an anticline may be eroded away, with the anticline sometimes continuing underground. Petroleum and natural gas may be trapped at the crest of a water-bearing rock layer that is enclosed by two impermeable (solid) rock layers. An impermeable rock is one that forms a barrier to water.

ANTICYCLONE An anticyclone, or high, is a large moving area of high barometric pressure that is marked by clear skies and low humidity. Wind circulates in a clockwise direction around a high-pressure center in the Northern Hemisphere. In the Southern Hemisphere, it circulates in a counterclockwise direction.

An anticyclone is the opposite of a cyclone, or low. A cyclone is a large moving area of air that is marked by low barometric pressure, cloudy skies, and precipitation (see CYCLONE).

Anticyclones move from west to east across the United States. They travel slowly and can remain stationary for several days. Cumulus, or fair-weather clouds, can form in an anticyclone (see CLOUD). Smog can occur over densely populated areas when winds are too light to blow away exhaust smoke from cars and factories (see SMOG).

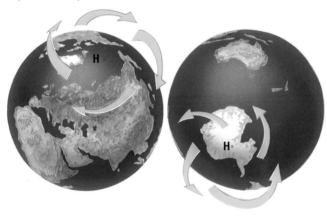

ANTICYCLONE

In the diagrams above, the H stands for high barometric pressure. Wind circulates around a high-pressure center: clockwise in the Northern Hemisphere (left) and counterclockwise in the Southern Hemisphere (right).

Anticyclones in temperate regions are characterized by sinking air, clear skies, and wind. Again, the H stands for high barometric pressure.

Summer anticyclones in temperate regions feature warm temperatures, clear skies, and light winds. Winter anticyclones have low temperatures, clear skies, and strong winds. A Bermuda high is an anticyclone that affects the eastern part of the United States several times each summer. It is a stationary high, centered near Bermuda, an island east of North Carolina. The Bermuda high brings warm, humid air from the Caribbean area into the southeastern and eastern states.

Permanent anticyclones can form over land and ocean areas. Much of Siberia is covered by a large anticyclone every winter.

The so-called horse latitudes of the oceans, 30°N and 30°S, have permanent anticyclones. They create trade winds—steady breezes that blow in one direction for weeks at a time. When sailing ships were common, they used these winds to cross the oceans.

See also AIR; WEATHER; WIND.

ANTIDOTE An antidote is a remedy for a particular poison. Antidotes generally react chemically with the poison to make it harmless and so prevent it from taking effect on the body. There are only specific antidotes for about five percent of poisons.

Most antidotes are used to combat the poisonous bites of certain animals. These antidotes are called antivenoms. There are antivenoms available to treat the bites and stings of venomous snakes (vipers, cobras, and sea-snakes), scorpions, and spiders, especially the black widow spider of North America and the tropics, and the brown recluse spider of the southern United States.

Venomous jellyfish and sea anemones have tentacles that contain a powerful alkaline toxin. The poisonous effect of a sting from these animals can be neutralized by washing acetic acid (vinegar) over the area that has been in contact with the tentacles.

See also DRUGS; POISON.

ANTIFREEZE An antifreeze is a substance that, when added to a liquid, lowers the freezing point of that liquid. The main ingredient of an antifreeze is usually a type of alcohol (see ALCO-HOL).

Ethylene glycol is the basis of the most common antifreeze. It is used in the cooling systems of internal combustion engines, such as those in many automobiles. During the cold winter months, this antifreeze is used alone or with water to prevent the freezing of the cooling system. Methanol is also sometimes used as an antifreeze in internal combustion engines. These antifreezes are often drained out of the cooling system after the threat of freezing is over. Often, because of evaporation, antifreeze loses its power. It can also creep into the block of an engine and cause problems in lubrication.

Ethylene glycol is also used to prevent icing of propellers and wings of airplanes. Glycerol and ethyl alcohol are used to protect drugs and cosmetics from freezing during storage. Calcium chloride and sodium chloride, unlike other antifreezes, are salts used in refrigeration.

ANTIHISTAMINE Antihistamine drugs block the action of histamine, which is a substance that can cause allergic reactions in certain people. In hay fever, one of the most common allergies, dust and pollen affect the mucous cells lining the nose and throat. These cells start to release histamine, which causes the sufferer watery eyes, a runny nose, and sneezing.

Early antihistamines caused drowsiness because they were able to affect the brain, but the more modern drugs such as astemizole and cetirizine remain in the blood and are more effective in controlling hay-fever symptoms without side-effects.
See also ALLERGY.

ANTIMATTER All matter is made up of very small particles called elementary particles. For example, the outer parts of atoms consist of particles called electrons. The inner parts, or nuclei, are made up of protons and neutrons (see ATOM). The protons and neutrons are made up of still smaller particles called quarks (see QUARK).

Each elementary particle has a corresponding antiparticle. The antiparticle is almost identical to the ordinary particle. It has the same mass, but some other properties, such as electric charge or spin, are reversed. For example, an electron has a negative charge. Its antiparticle is called a positron, and it has a positive charge. Antiparticles can be produced in reactions in particle accelerators and can be found in cosmic rays (see ACCELERATORS, PARTICLE).

Sometimes a particle and its antiparticle collide. When they do so, they destroy each other. The particle and its antiparticle disappear, and radiation in the form of gamma rays is produced. For example, positrons are produced by radioactive substances and in cosmic rays (see COSMIC RAYS; RADIOACTIVITY). They soon collide with electrons and both are destroyed.

Antiparticles make up antimatter. It was once suggested that whole galaxies far off in the universe might be made of antimatter, but this is no longer thought likely.

The Big Bang theory suggests that the universe was created by a single huge explosion. Physicists think that this explosion produced both matter and antimatter. Particles and antiparticles collided and vanished, creating huge amounts of radiation. There was very slightly more matter than antimatter to begin with, and so some matter was left over. This matter makes up the universe today.
See also ATOM; COSMOLOGY; PARTICLE PHYSICS.

ANTISEPTIC An antiseptic is a chemical that either kills or stops the growth of microorganisms on living tissue. It is different from a disinfectant, which destroys microorganisms on nonliving objects (see DISINFECTANT; MICROORGANISM).

Antiseptics are used in operating rooms of hospitals to make sure no microorganisms can enter the patients' bodies and cause infection. First-aid medicine includes antiseptics to kill any microorganism that may be present on the skin around a cut.
See also ASEPSIS; INFECTION.

ANTITOXIN Organisms make antitoxins to protect themselves against toxins. A toxin is a chemical that is poisonous to an organism. Most

ANTLER

Antlers grown by deer provide weapons for defense and mating battles. In some species, both females and males grow antlers. In most species of deer, however, only the males grow them. New antlers grow each year, starting in summer. They are shed in spring.

toxins are proteins. Most antitoxins are antibodies, which are also proteins. Certain bacteria, snakes, and other organisms make toxins that are dangerous to humans. For example, the bacteria that cause diphtheria and tetanus produce toxins that can kill a human. The human body produces many antitoxins to neutralize (make harmless) toxins that are produced by disease-causing bacteria. When a person does not have enough antitoxin in his or her blood, a doctor will inject some from another animal to help the person fight the toxins.

See also ANTIBODY; IMMUNITY.

ANTLER Antlers are bone growths from the heads of most male deer and some female deer. The only male deer without antlers are the Chinese water deer and the musk deer. The caribou and reindeer are the only kinds of deer in which both the males and females have antlers. Antlers are used for defense. They are also used during the mating season, when male deer fight head-on for female mates.

Unlike the horns of other animals, deer antlers are solid bone. Horns are hollow, bony growths with a skinlike covering. Antlers are part of the skeleton. Horns are not part of the skeleton.

Deer lose their antlers every spring after the mating season. New antlers grow during the summer, fall, and winter months. At first, the new antlers are covered with a velvety skin. When the antlers are fully developed, this covering dries and cracks. Deer rub their antlers against trees to rid their antlers of the dead tissue.

The moose is the largest member of the deer family. Its antlers sometimes grow to 6 ft. [1.8 m] in width. Other deer antlers range from short and spiky to long and branched.

In prehistoric times, humans made tools out of antlers. In China, antlers are still used in the making of some medicines.

The size of antlers is usually determined by the age of a deer. When some deer get very old, their antlers become smaller. A deer's health and the environment it lives in also determine the size and condition of its antlers.

See also DEER.

ANUS (ā′nəs) The anus is the opening at the lower end of the alimentary canal. All organisms with a complete digestive system have a mouth through which food can be taken and an anus through which solid wastes, called feces, pass from the body. Anal sphincter muscles surround the anus of most animals. These muscles control the release of feces by controlling the opening and closing of the anus. A baby does not have control over the anal sphincter muscles. Control of them is voluntary and must be learned.

See also ALIMENTARY CANAL; INTESTINE.

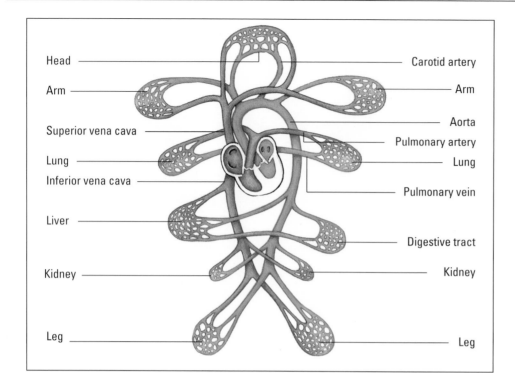

Head — Carotid artery

Arm — Arm

Superior vena cava — Aorta

— Pulmonary artery

Lung — Lung

Inferior vena cava — Pulmonary vein

Liver — Digestive tract

Kidney — Kidney

Leg — Leg

AORTA

The aorta is the main artery that distributes blood containing lots of oxygen to the rest of the body. Smaller arteries branch off it as it leaves the heart and travels down through the chest and abdomen.

AORTA (ā ôr′tə) The aorta is the largest and longest artery in the human body. It carries oxygen-rich blood away from the heart to the other major arteries. The aorta starts in the left ventricle of the heart and rises to near the bottom of the neck. It then arches backward and downward through the chest and abdomen. Arteries branch off the aorta along its entire length. These arteries supply blood to the heart muscle, the brain, and all other body tissue.

See also ARTERY; CIRCULATORY SYSTEM; HEART.

APATITE Apatite is the name for a group of common minerals containing calcium phosphate. Apatite also contains chlorine or fluorine. Its name comes from the Greek word *apate*, meaning "deception." The mineral is well named, as apatite may look like several other minerals. Its crystals may be brown, yellow, green, blue, violet, white, or even colorless. Apatite is found in many kinds of rocks. In North America, Florida is the main source of apatite. Other large deposits are found in Russia and North Africa.

Apatite has hardness 5 on the Mohs scale (see HARDNESS). Apatite is used in the making of fertilizer and phosphoric acid.

See also PHOSPHORIC ACID.

APE

The gorilla (pictured), chimpanzees, orangutans, and gibbons are all apes. In the animal kingdom, apes are probably second in intelligence only to human beings.

APE Apes are primates belonging to the family Pongidae. Apes have long arms, fingers, and toes. They have hairy bodies with no tails. Apes have large brains and are probably second in intelligence only to human beings. Apes live in tropical areas of Asia and Africa. The so-called great apes include chimpanzees, gorillas, and orangutans. The smaller, lesser apes include the six kinds of gibbons. Monkeys are different from apes because monkeys have tails and do not walk upright.

Apes look similar to human beings. Apes, though, do not stand completely upright. *See also* ANTHROPOID.

APHID (ā′fĭd) Aphids, or plant lice, are small, soft-bodied insects that damage plants. Aphids have a needle-shaped mouth that they use to suck out plant juices. Aphids can often spread disease from one plant to another. Aphids may be any of several colors, but most are green or black. The male usually has four wings. The female is often wingless. Aphids belong to the insect group known as the Homoptera.

After mating in the fall, the female lays her eggs. These eggs hatch in the spring. The newborn aphids, which are females, then give birth to other living aphids from unfertilized eggs within their own bodies. This form of reproduction, called parthenogenesis, produces many aphids each summer (see PARTHENOGENESIS).

Some kinds of aphids have a symbiotic relationship with ants (see SYMBIOSIS). The aphids produce a sweet, waxy fluid called honeydew, which ants like to eat. Ants protect the aphids in exchange for this honeydew.

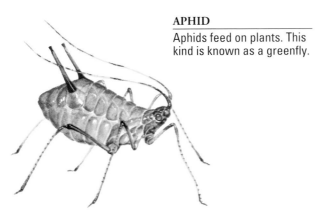

APHID
Aphids feed on plants. This kind is known as a greenfly.

APOLLO PROJECT—Tests
One of the main functions of the manned trips to the moon was to gather samples and to take measurements of such things as gravity and solar radiation. Here an astronaut on the Apollo 12 mission sets up a solar-powered testing device.

APOLLO PROJECT Apollo was the name of a large spaceflight project involving thousands of scientists, astronauts, technicians, and manufacturers assembled by NASA (National Aeronautics and Space Administration) in 1961. The aim of the project was to land men on the moon and bring them back safely before 1970. This goal was set by President John F. Kennedy on May 25, 1961, and unanimously approved by Congress.

Apollo beat its deadline by half a year. Civilian astronaut Neil Armstrong stepped from the lunar module *Eagle* onto the surface of the moon in July 1969.

There were many problems in the early stages of the project. A rocket powerful enough to reach the moon had to be designed and built. New launching, training, and research bases were needed. A worldwide radio tracking network had to be set up.

The method chosen for the attempt at landing on the moon was called lunar orbit rendezvous. Three astronauts would travel to the moon in a three-part spacecraft. The crew would live in the command module. The service module would

APOLLO PROJECT—Lunar landing

Astronauts on the Apollo 11 mission in 1969 (the first lunar landing mission) were aided in their work by the lunar module (LM) *Eagle* seen to the left of the flag. It carried astronauts down to the surface and was to take them back to the orbiting command module. Footprints of the astronauts are clearly visible in the soil of the moon.

APOLLO PROJECT—After splashdown

United States Navy divers prepare the Apollo 8 spacecraft for hoisting aboard the U.S.S. *Yorktown* after landing on December 27, 1968.

hold necessary equipment. The third part was the lunar module.

The whole spacecraft would orbit, or circle, the moon at great height. Two astronauts would climb into the lunar module (LM) and use it to go down to the surface of the moon. Later, a part of the LM would bring the astronauts back to the command and service modules. The LM would be discarded before the spacecraft returned to Earth.

On January 27, 1967, Apollo had a serious setback. Astronauts Virgil Grissom, Edward White, and Roger Chaffee were burned to death in a fire aboard the spacecraft during a practice session. The spacecraft had to be redesigned. Flight testing resumed in October 1968, with the Earth-orbital mission, Apollo 7.

During December 1968, the first flight around the moon took place when astronauts Frank Borman, James Lovell, and William Anders circled the moon ten times, transmitting a special television program on the occasion of Christmas.

On July 20, 1969, Armstrong and Edwin Aldrin landed on the moon in an area known as the Sea of Tranquillity. Michael Collins remained aboard the Apollo 11 command module in orbit. Armstrong and Aldrin stayed on the moon for 21 hours, 35 minutes.

In November 1969, the Apollo 12 team landed Charles Conrad and Alan Bean on the moon, with Richard Gordon remaining on board the orbiting spacecraft. In April 1970, an explosion ripped open the service module of Apollo 13 when it was 200,000 mi. [320,000 km] from Earth. The crew and spacecraft were successfully brought back to Earth.

Four successful Apollo moon landings followed. The last three lunar landing missions each carried a battery-powered four-wheeled car, the lunar rover, to let the astronauts do part of their exploring by driving rather than by walking. The final landing, Apollo 17, happened on December 11, 1972. Eugene Cernan and Harrison Schmitt spent 74 hours, 59 minutes on the moon and returned with 250 lb. [113 kg] of lunar material, while Ronald Evans stayed in the orbiting command module.

See also ARMSTRONG, NEIL ALDEN; MOON; SPACE EXPLORATION.

APPENDIX The appendix is a part of the intestines in humans. Its full name is the vermiform appendix. The appendix is found on the lower right side of the abdomen. It is about 1 to 6 in. [2.5 to 15.25 cm] in length. The appendix is attached to the cecum. The cecum is the first part of the large intestine.

Although the appendix does not serve a useful purpose today, it was probably a necessary part of the digestive system thousands of years ago. The human diet was different then from what it is now, and digestion of those different foods may have made the appendix necessary.

See also DIGESTION; INTESTINE.

APPLE An apple is the fruit of about twenty-five species of trees belonging to the rose family, Rosaceae (see ROSE FAMILY). There are thousands of kinds of apples in three categories: cooking apples, cider apples, and dessert apples. When ripe, apples are usually red, yellow, or green. They have round shapes and measure 2 to 4 in. [5 to 10 cm] in diameter.

Apples grow in most parts of the United States and the rest of the world. Apple trees require long dormancy, which means that some period of relatively cold weather is needed. Apples cannot usually be grown in tropical places (see DORMANCY).

Scientists believe the apple originated thou-

APPLE

An apple is the fruit of a tree belonging to the rose family. Apples are rich in vitamins A and C.

sands of years ago in Turkey as the fruit of a wild roselike shrub. Since then, humans have developed that wild plant into the many kinds of apple trees we know today.

Apples contain vitamins A and C. They are good sources of dietary fiber and are high in carbohydrates.

APRICOT An apricot is the fruit of a tree belonging to the rose family, Rosaceae (see ROSE FAMILY). It has a smooth pit called a stone at its

APRICOT

The apricot is believed to have originated in China thousands of years ago. It is a delicious and nourishing fruit, both fresh and dried.

center. It looks like a yellow peach except that its skin is not fuzzy like that of a peach. Apricot trees grow best in fairly warm places. These trees resist drought well. They can live as long as one hundred years.

An apricot can be eaten fresh as a dessert fruit. It also can be preserved by canning or drying. Apricots are a good source of vitamin A. Dried apricots are an excellent source of iron.

Scientists believe the apricot tree originated in China thousands of years ago. Today, it grows throughout the earth's mild climate zones. Spain is the world's leading producer of apricots. Most of the apricots grown in the United States come from California.

AQUATIC PLANT

An aquatic plant is a plant or plantlike organism that lives in water. It is also called a *hydrophyte*, which means "water plant." There are many different forms of aquatic plants. They may belong to many different divisions of the plant kingdom and other kingdoms. Submerged plants are species that live completely under water. Most of the algae (members of kingdom Monera) are examples of this form. Floating plants float freely on the surface of the water. Duckweed and wolffia are floating plants. Emergent plants have their roots and bases in the water but grow leaves above the water surface. A cattail plant is a tall, emergent plant.

Plants that live in the water must adapt to conditions that do not exist on land. Submerged leaves and stems of aquatic plants do not have a thick, waxy cuticle, or film, to prevent evaporation as do land plants (see LEAF). Many submerged plants do not have roots. They must absorb water and minerals through the leaf surface. Some algae that are exposed at low tide are covered with mucus to prevent their drying out.

The pollen of flowering plants on land is spread by wind and insects (see POLLINATION). This cannot occur with submerged flowering plants. These species have developed methods of underwater pollination.

Aquatic plants are important members of the water environment. They supply food, shelter,

AQUATIC PLANT

Aquatic plants (which include organisms that are plantlike but do not belong to the plant kingdom) are found throughout the world. They grow in both freshwater and marine (seawater) environments. These are water lilies.

and oxygen for many animals. However, if aquatic plants grow too plentiful, they can clog waterways and cause other problems. This overgrowth is sometimes the result of water pollution.

AQUEDUCT

An aqueduct is an artificial channel that carries water from one place to another. It can consist of a pipeline above or below the ground, a tunnel, or an open ditch. It may also be a bridgelike structure that carries water across a valley. Water moves through an aqueduct either by means of gravity or under pressure from pumps. Aqueducts are used to bring drinking water to cities and irrigation water to farmland. They are also used in hydroelectric projects (see HYDROELECTRIC POWER).

AQUEDUCT

The Romans built aqueducts to bring water into Rome from the surrounding hills. The first of them, the Aqua Appia, was built in 312 B.C. by the politician Appius Claudius.

The aqueducts that are used to bring drinking water to cities can be hundreds of miles long. The longest aqueduct in the world is the California State Water Project Aqueduct. It is 826 mi. [1,329 km] long, of which 385 mi. [619 km] has canals.

The Romans built large aqueducts in Europe more than two thousand years ago. The remains of many of these are still standing.

See also IRRIGATION.

AQUIFER (ăk′wə fər) An aquifer is a layer of gravel, sand, or other porous underground rock, such as limestone, in which groundwater settles. Aquifers are important underground water reservoirs in many areas. Many places get their water from wells that have been drilled down into aquifers.

During the 1980s, scientists began to be concerned about the rising number of aquifers being polluted by chemicals. The sources of these pollutants include pits where garbage has been dumped, sewage from cities, underground chemical-waste disposal sites, and underground gasoline-storage tanks that have leaks. Some coastal communities have also seen the contamination by ocean salts in the aquifers from which they draw their water. Ocean water has seeped in because the overdeveloped coastal communities drained most of the fresh water out of the aquifer.

In other communities, such as Phoenix and Tucson in Arizona, aquifers are simply drying up because of overuse by heavily populated communities and by farmers. Unless strong regulations are adopted to curb groundwater contamination, the world's supply of safe drinking water will be at risk.

See also GROUNDWATER; POLLUTION.

PROJECT 17

ARACHNID (ə răk′nĭd) Arachnids are a class of animals in the group of joint-legged creatures called Arthropoda. The arachnids include spiders, harvestmen ("daddy longlegs"), ticks, mites, and scorpions. They have four pairs of legs, two-part bodies, no antennae, and no wings. They also have two small fangs at the front of their heads. With the exception of a few mites, all arachnids are carnivorous (meat-eaters), but they do not eat solid food. Instead, they extract fluids from their food.

There are several differences between insects and arachnids. Arachnids have two more legs than insects. Insects, unlike arachnids, have antennae and often have wings.

See also ARTHROPODA; INSECT; PARASITE.

ARACHNID

Spiders, scorpions, and harvestmen (clockwise from left) are all arachnids. Arachnids are a widespread class of arthropods. Many arachnids are helpful to humans because they eat large quantities of insect pests.

ARBORETUM

Morton Aboretum, in Illinois, displays many fine specimen trees from a wide range of species. The colorful changes in foliage can be seen from spring (top) to fall (bottom).

ARBORETUM (är′bə rē′təm) An arboretum is a garden where woody plants such as trees and shrubs are grown for decorative, educational, or scientific purposes. Arboretums can cover several acres. The first arboretum was founded in France during the mid-1500s. Some of the best-known arboretums in the United States are Brooklyn Botanical Garden (Brooklyn, New York), National Arboretum (Washington, D.C.), and Morton Arboretum (Lisle, Illinois).

ARBORVITAE (är′bər vī′tē) Arborvitae is a common name for a group of evergreen trees that belong to the genus *Thuja* in the cypress family. *Arborvitae* means "tree of life" in Latin. Early

ARBORVITAE

The western red cedar is an evergreen belonging to the cypress family. The common name for this group of trees is *arborvitae*, which means "tree of life."

European explorers of North America gave the trees this name. When the explorers were visiting the area now known as Canada, they suffered from the disease scurvy. The native North Americans made a tea from the arborvitae tree. This tea helped restore the explorers' health. The two North American species of arborvitae are also known as northern white cedar and western red cedar. However, they are not true cedars. True cedars belong to the pine family.

See also SCURVY.

ARC, ELECTRIC

An electric arc is a curve of light and heat that forms when a strong electric current leaps across a gap between two electrodes. The electrodes are usually metal or carbon. The electric arc is a stream of electrons and ions passing between the electrodes. The arc gives out light and heat because electrons hit molecules of gases in the air between the electrodes.

The light from electric arcs is very bright. Commercially manufactured arc lights give a very white light from an arc between two carbon electrodes. Arc lights have been used in television and film studios and in searchlights.

When an electric arc passes between two electrodes, the electrodes become very hot. Arc fur-

naces use arcs to melt steel and other metals. Arc welding uses an electric arc to melt and join metals.

See also ELECTRICITY; ELECTRODE; ELECTRON; IONS AND IONIZATION.

ARCH

In construction, an arch is a curved structure built to support weight above an opening. The most common uses for arches are in bridges; in supports for roadways and railroad tracks; and in windows, doorways, and passageways in buildings. Arches can be made of many substances, including stone, steel, concrete, timber, and even aluminum.

The world's oldest arches were built by the ancient Romans. Around 300 B.C., the ancient Romans used the arch to build bridges and aqueducts. The world's longest span of arches is the Rockville Bridge, north of Harrisburg, in Pennsylvania. The bridge has 48 spans and is 3,810 ft. [1,161 m] long.

Arches can also be built by nature. Natural arches take hundreds and even thousands of years to form. A natural arch is formed when water flows slowly through soil or porous rock that has a harder rock layer above it. The harder rock stays firm, and the soil or porous rock is slowly carried away with the water. The Landscape Arch in the Arches National Park near Moab in Utah is the world's longest, at 291 ft. [88 m].

ARCH

The development of the arch by the ancient Romans was one of the most important advances in building technology.

ARCHAEOPTERYX

The *Archaeopteryx* is the earliest known bird. Scientists believe that this animal evolved from a small carnivorous (meat-eating) dinosaur.

ARCHAEOPTERYX (är´kē ŏp´tər ĭks) The *Archaeopteryx* is the earliest known bird. The word *Archaeopteryx* means "ancient wing." The *Archaeopteryx* evolved from reptiles and lived during the time of the dinosaurs, about 140 million years ago. The first fossil remains of the *Archaeopteryx* were found in Germany in the 1800s.

The *Archaeopteryx* was about 20 in. [51 cm] long. The *Archaeopteryx* did not fly very well and probably only for short distances. Its wing muscles were not very large. Unlike the *Pterodactylus*, or flying reptile, the *Archaeopteryx* flapped its wings. The *Pterodactylus* was a glider and did not flap its wings.

The skeleton of an *Archaeopteryx* is like the skeleton of a small, carnivorous (meat-eating) dinosaur. Unlike dinosaurs, which had scales, the *Archaeopteryx* had feathers. The *Archaeopteryx* was unlike modern birds because it had teeth, a long bony tail, and three clawed "fingers" at the end of each of its two wings. The *Archaeopteryx* probably used its fingers and feet for climbing.

See also DINOSAUR; PTERODACTYLUS.

ARCHEGONIUM (är´kĭ gō´nē əm) An archegonium is the female sex organ in certain plants, such as liverworts, mosses, ferns, and conifers. It is bottle shaped with a long, thin neck. In the base of the archegonium is the egg. The male sex organ, the antheridium, produces a sperm that enters the neck of the archegonium. The sperm travels down into the base where it joins with the egg. The fertilized egg is called a zygote. The zygote will develop into a new organism, which will disperse itself either by developing seeds or spores.

See also ANTHERIDIUM; REPRODUCTION.

ARCHEOLOGY Archeology is the scientific study of the physical traces of people of the past. It deals with objects made by people and with the remains of people, plants, and animals. These objects and remains often must be dug up from beneath the earth or water. The purpose of archeology is to explain what people were like in the past and how they lived.

Persons who work in archeology are called archeologists. They often have been trained in other sciences, such as anthropology, biology, geology, and zoology, as well. They use picks and shovels as well as microscopes and radioactivity testing in their work.

The first thing an archeologist must do is search for the places where people of the past have lived. The archeologist is like a detective who must solve a mystery. He or she searches for camps, houses, villages, and cities that might be buried. An archeologist also explores caves and underground cemeteries.

The things that archeologists find become pieces of a puzzle. They tell a story of the past. All of the puzzle's pieces cannot always be found. Stone and metal objects may be found. The bones of humans and animals are sometimes found. Fossils are often found (see FOSSIL). Some things, however, are lost to decomposition, or decay. Items made of straw, cloth, or wood are rarely found. Burned wood in the form of charcoal is very valuable to an archeologist. It is wood that has not decomposed, permitting an archeologist

to decide the amount of time that has gone by since its origin.

Archeologists carefully study the objects they find. They also make detailed records of where these objects were found and what they look like. Archeologists use these studies to establish information about people who lived hundreds or thousands of years ago. For example, carvings on pots tell archeologists about the kind of art people produced. The construction of their houses and the form of their tools and weapons tell about their building and craft-working skills. Bones of animals might tell what kind of food they ate.

Archeology began in the 1500s, when the people of Europe became interested in the ancient civilizations of Rome, Greece, and Egypt. Thomas Jefferson of the United States studied Native American mounds in Virginia in 1784. His archeology is considered the first to be done in the modern or scientific way. Archeology before that was mainly a hunt for things to sell to museums and collectors. Unscientific archeology of this sort destroyed things that modern archeologists would have saved. Archeologists today are going back over some of the diggings of earlier archeologists to check for mistakes. Since the 1930s, archeology has become a precise science with strict rules and procedures.

Some of the most famous finds of archeology are the Rosetta Stone of Egypt and the Dead Sea Scrolls of Israel. The Rosetta Stone was found in 1799. It was the chief clue to understanding hieroglyphics, which are the symbols of the written language of ancient Egypt. The Dead Sea Scrolls were found in 1947. They are the first known writings of the Bible. In the United States, archeologists are often called to places where construction workers uncover signs of old Native American life. In Central and South America, archeologists have uncovered the ruins of great Indian civilizations.

Modern technology has advanced archeology. Scientists today are able to determine the age of archeological objects by using chemistry and electronics. Some prehistoric objects are tested for radiocarbon, potassium, and argon content. Instruments for measuring these contents can sometimes tell archeologists how many thousands or millions of years the object has been in its present form.

See also ANTHROPOLOGY; DATING.

ARCHEOZOIC ERA

ARCHEOZOIC ERA The Archeozoic era is the period in the earth's history to which the oldest rocks and the earliest known forms of life belong. It followed the Azoic era, which started when the earth was formed. The Archeozoic era ended about 1.85 billion years ago, when the Proterozoic era began. Lava rocks from the Archeozoic era, dating from one to two billion years ago, are found all over the world.

During the Archeozoic era, the oldest mountains in North America—the Laurentians in Canada—were formed. Radioactive dating has shown rocks of the Archeozoic era to be at the base of the Adirondacks, the Colorado Rocky Mountains, and in the Grand Canyon.

The first known signs of life on Earth, the algae, were found fossilized in Archeozoic rocks in Africa. These fossils are believed to be about 3.5 billion years old. Fossils dating back to about that time have also been found in Australia and North America.

See also GEOLOGICAL TIME SCALE.

ARCHERFISH The archerfish is generally a freshwater fish that belongs to the family Toxotidae, although there are some saltwater species. It is found in the warm coastal waters and river mouths of India and Indonesia. It has an elongated body, flattened from the dorsal fin forwards, and can grow up to 7 in. (18 cm) in length (see FISH). Some species are spotted while others have vertical black stripes.

The archerfish gets its name from the way it captures food. It has a deep groove running along the roof of its mouth, which it can make into a tube by covering the groove with its flexible tongue. When the fish sees an insect sitting on a leaf above the water, the fish squirts water at the insect. The water knocks the insect into the water. The archerfish then eats the fallen insect.

ARCHIMEDES (är′kə mē′dēz′) (about 287–212 B.C.) Archimedes, called the "father of experimental science," was an ancient Greek physicist, mathematician, and inventor. Among other things, Archimedes studied the use of levers and pulleys to lift heavy objects, such as large ships. He is said to have learned how to pump water uphill by using a device now called Archimedes' screw, though it was probably invented long before him (see ARCHIMEDES' SCREW). In the field of mathematics, he found out how to measure the area of circles and other figures. He worked out a value for pi (π) and came close to inventing calculus.

Archimedes spent most of his life in Syracuse, a city in Sicily, which is an island of Italy. Here he discovered a famous law (now called Archimedes' principle), which states that when a solid object is immersed in a liquid, it is pushed up by a force equal to the weight of the liquid that has been displaced by the object. It is said that Archimedes discovered this principle in a strange way. According to the story, the king of Syracuse asked Archimedes to tell him if his new crown was pure gold. Archimedes thought of a way to test the crown. He had noticed that when he stepped into a full bathtub, the tub overflowed. His body had displaced a certain amount of water. He realized that if the crown were pure gold it would displace the same amount of water as a chunk of pure gold weighing the same as the crown. He made the test and discovered that the crown was not pure gold. The goldsmith had cheated the king.

Archimedes designed war machines for the king. According to another of the many stories about him, he invented giant mirrors to focus the sun's rays in order to burn enemy ships attacking Syracuse. Archimedes' genius helped the king hold off his enemies for three years. Archimedes is said to have been killed during the final battle for the city, when the Romans took over Syracuse.

See also BUOYANCY; RELATIVE DENSITY.

 PROJECT 3

ARCHIMEDES' SCREW An Archimedes' screw is a device used to raise water. The invention is credited to the Greek mathematician and inventor Archimedes. The device consists of a helical screw which fits tightly inside a cylinder. The whole device is set at an angle with one end submerged in the water. As a handle connected to the top of the screw is turned, the screw rotates inside the cylinder and the water is carried upwards.

See also ARCHIMEDES.

One percent of the air is argon. Argon can be obtained from the air by separating it from the other gases. This is done by liquefying the air. The argon is then separated by distillation (see DISTILLATION).

Argon has an atomic number of 18 and a relative atomic mass of 39.95. It boils at -303°F [-186°C] and melts at -308°F [-189°C]. It was discovered in 1894 by the British scientists Sir William Ramsay and Lord Rayleigh.
See also RAMSAY, SIR WILLIAM.

ARISTOTLE
The writings of Aristotle covered almost every field of knowledge, as well as subjects such as poetry and politics.

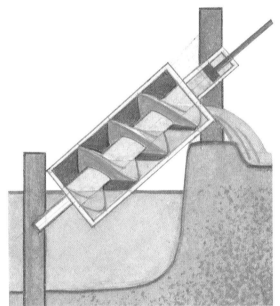

ARCHIMEDES' SCREW
The Archimedes' screw pumps water upwards by forcing it up a pipe when a screw inside the pipe is turned. The screw was once used to pump water out of ships. Today it is still used to pump water out of streams for irrigating crops.

ARGON Argon is a colorless, odorless, gaseous element. Its symbol is Ar. Argon is one of the noble gases (see NOBLE GAS). This means that it is chemically inactive. It does not combine easily with other elements. Because of this, it is used in electric light bulbs. A more reactive gas would attack the hot filament.

ARISTOTLE (384–322 B.C.) Aristotle was a Greek philosopher and scientist who developed many ideas about the nature of life and matter. He also wrote on literature, politics, and ethics. He introduced logic, or systematic reasoning, into science. This was important because it allowed scientists to verify, or test the truth of, their ideas by observation. Aristotle did much work in biology and zoology. He was the first person to classify animals on the basis of structure and behavior. Aristotle stated that dolphins are mammals, not fish. This idea was not believed for hundreds of years, until proven in the 1800s. He also put forward some of the first ideas on human evolution.

Aristotle's theories were widely believed in the Middle Ages. Some of his ideas may have kept science from moving forward during that period. For instance, Aristotle mistakenly thought that heavy objects fall faster than light objects. He also believed that the sun revolved around the earth. In the 1500s and 1600s, scientists such as Newton, Galileo, and Copernicus proved these ideas wrong.
See also COPERNICUS; GALILEO; NEWTON, SIR ISAAC.

ARITHMETIC Arithmetic is the branch of mathematics that studies numbers and computations performed on numbers, such as addition and subtraction. A young child who counts on his or her fingers is doing arithmetic. The child can see that his or her hands have five fingers each and that each foot has five toes.

It is easy to see if two groups of objects have the same number of features. Match each object in the first group with one from the second. A group of five sheep, the fingers on one hand, and a pile of five marbles all have something in common, which is the number five.

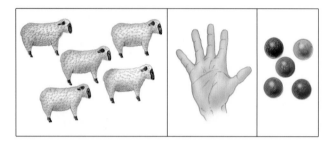

The number of fingers was probably the basis of arithmetic, explaining why number systems often use groups of fives or tens. A simple way of recording numbers may be by using objects such as marbles. This becomes a problem, however, when dealing in large numbers. A better way is to use symbols in place of objects.

One example of an early system of arithmetic is the ancient Roman system. This system was very simple, using only a few symbols. For example, 15 would be written as ten (X) with five (V), or XV. 378 would be written as CCCLXXVIII. However, it was very complicated to multiply and divide using Roman numerals.

Roman numerals	I	V	X	L	C	D	M
Value	1	5	10	50	100	500	1000

The number system we now use comes from the Hindu-Arabic numerals. This system uses the symbols 1, 2, 3, 4, 5, 6, 7, 8, 9, and 0. Using these ten numerals, it is possible to write any number by combining the symbols in different ways. The position of the symbol tells whether it is of units, tens, hundreds, and so on. For example, in the number 238, the 8 stands for eight units, the 3 for three tens, and the 2 for two hundreds. A symbol for zero is necessary in order to tell the differences among twenty-three (23), two hundred three (203), and two hundred thirty (230). The development of zero as a placeholder was a major development in the history of numbers.

Tens	Units
2	3

Hundreds	Tens	Units
2	0	3

Hundreds	Tens	Units
2	3	0

Two groups of things can be combined to make a larger group. When this is done, it is called addition, the basis of arithmetic. Adding can be done by counting the amount of the first number, and then counting on from the first number an amount equal to the second number.

Our system groups numbers in tens. It is possible to add the units together, and then the tens, the hundreds, and so on. The diagram shows what happens when 26 and 38 are added together. The 6 and 8 give a total of 14, or a group of ten and four units. This means a total of six groups of ten altogether, with four units, written as 64.

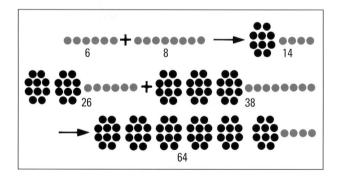

The inverse of addition is subtraction. To subtract one number from another, a person may think in terms of addition. For example, the problem, "What does 8 become when 5 is subtracted from it?" may be thought of as, "What number added to 5 gets 8?" The statement 8 - 5 = 3 is true because 3 + 5 = 8.

Multiplying two numbers together may be shown by a process of repeated addition. 5 x 4 means four groups of five added together, or 5 + 5 + 5 + 5. This problem may also be seen as five groups of 4 added together, or 4 + 4 + 4 + 4 + 4. Tables for multiplication can be worked out by repeated addition. An easy way to set out the tables is in the form of a square.

X	1	2	3	4	5	6	7	8	9
1	1	2	3	4	5	6	7	8	9
2	2	4	6	8	10	12	14	16	18
3	3	6	9	12	15	18	21	24	27
4	4	8	12	16	20	24	28	32	36
5	5	10	15	20	25	30	35	40	45
6	6	12	18	24	30	36	42	48	54
7	7	14	21	28	35	42	49	56	63
8	8	16	24	32	40	48	56	64	72
9	9	18	27	36	45	54	63	72	81

Square numbers are numbers produced by taking any number and multiplying that number by itself—for example, 1 x 1 = 1, 2 x 2 = 4, 3 x 3 = 9, and 4 x 4 = 16. Square numbers can be shown as sets of dots arranged in squares. An interesting pattern appears in going from one square number to the next.

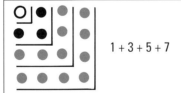

1 = 1
4 = 1 + 3
9 = 1 + 3 + 5
16 = 1 + 3 + 5 + 7

1 + 3 + 5 + 7

The triangular numbers are 1, 3, 6, 10, and so on. It is easy to spot the pattern formed by moving from one triangular number to the next.

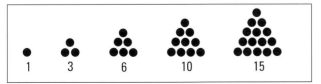

1   3   6   10   15

The following diagram shows an interesting connection between the triangular numbers and the square numbers.

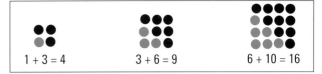

1 + 3 = 4   3 + 6 = 9   6 + 10 = 16

Rectangular numbers can be arranged as a number of equal rows. 12 can be shown as 3 rows of 4 or 2 rows of 6.

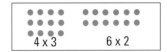

4 x 3   6 x 2

Some numbers can by shown only as a single row of dots. These numbers have only 1 and themselves as factors. They are called prime numbers. Whenever a number divides evenly into another number, it is called a factor.

The fourth operation of arithmetic is division. "What is 24 divided by 6?" may be thought of in terms of multiplication, or "What number multiplied by 6 gets 24?"

The numbers used in this discussion of arithmetic were all whole numbers, called positive integers. There are many other kinds of numbers, such as fractions. For example, a cake can be cut into four equal pieces. Each piece is a fraction, or part, of the whole cake. Each piece is one-fourth, written as $^1/_4$, of the whole cake.

Another way to write fractions is to use decimal numbers. Decimal numbers are used partly because they are easy to multiply and divide. The fraction $^1/_4$ is written as 0.25 when written as a decimal number. The period in a decimal number is called a decimal point. The first figure after the decimal point shows how many tenths are in the number. The second figure shows how many hundredths, and so on.

Mathematicians took centuries to develop the methods now used in arithmetic. Everyone who goes to school learns arithmetic. It is a skill necessary in science, business, and everyday life.

ARMADILLO An armadillo is a mammal belonging to the order Edentata (see MAMMAL). It has a tough, hard covering that looks like plates of armor. These plates are called scutes. There are twenty kinds of armadillos. They can be found from the southern United States to Argentina. Armadillos are pinkish or brown in color.

ARMADILLO

Armadillos are mammals that have protective hard plates, known as scutes, on their skin.

Armadillos eat insects, spiders, earthworms, and land snails. They have long tongues for licking up their food. Armadillos cannot bite. They have small teeth at the backs of their mouths. They use their strong claws to dig tunnels and burrows in the ground.

The fairy armadillo is about 6 in. [15 cm] long. It is the smallest armadillo. The giant armadillo is about 5 ft. [1.5 m] long. It is the largest armadillo. The nine-banded armadillo is about 2 ft. [60 cm] long. It is the only kind of armadillo found in the United States. It lives chiefly in the most southern states, but scientists say it is moving northward. The nine-banded armadillo gets its name from the nine movable bands of armor on its body. Other kinds of armadillos have three to eighteen movable armor bands on their bodies. The nine-banded armadillo weighs abut 15 lb. [6.75 kg]. The female of this species gives birth to four babies, which are always of the same sex.

Some armadillos are killed or trapped because they damage crops. They also damage the foundations of buildings with their underground tunnels and burrows. Armadillos can carry the disease leprosy (see LEPROSY). Some people eat the armadillo's meat.

ARMSTRONG, NEIL ALDEN (1930–)

Neil Armstrong, an American astronaut, was the first person to set foot on the moon. On July 20, 1969, he and Edwin Aldrin, Jr., landed the Apollo 11 lunar module on the moon. Armstrong was commander of the mission. He stepped onto the moon at 10:56 P.M., eastern daylight-saving time. His words, radioed back to Earth, were, "That's one small step for a man, one giant leap for mankind."

Armstrong was born in Wapakoneta, Ohio. He received a degree in aeronautical engineering from Purdue University. He became a test pilot and flew research airplanes for NASA (National Aeronautics and Space Administration). The rocket-powered X-15 was one of the planes he tested. Armstrong and David R. Scott were the crew of the Gemini 8 flight in March 1966. The first space docking of two vehicles was made on this flight.

Armstrong resigned from NASA in 1971 and began teaching engineering at the University of Cincinnati.

See also APOLLO PROJECT.

ARMSTRONG, NEIL ALDEN

Neil Armstrong was a fighter pilot and then a test pilot, flying rocket planes, before going into space.

ARROW WORM Arrow worms are small sea creatures belonging to the phylum Chaetognatha. They range in length from 1 to 4 in. [3 to 10 cm]. Most kinds are transparent. They are one of the most abundant animals found in plankton. Arrow worms live at all depths in the ocean. There are about forty species of arrow worms in the world. *See also* PLANKTON.

ARSENIC Arsenic is an element whose symbol is As. Most arsenic compounds are very poisonous. Such compounds are used as insecticides, weed killers, and rat poisons (see COMPOUND; INSECTICIDE; POISON).

Arsenic has three different crystal forms, called allotropes. One of these allotropes, gray arsenic, is the ordinary, stable form. Gray arsenic is metallic. When heated, gray arsenic does not melt. It goes straight from a solid to a gas. This is called sublimation (see SUBLIMATION). Gray arsenic sublimes at 1,135°F [613°C]. In nature, arsenic is usually found in combination with sulfur, oxygen, or various metals. The main mineral that contains arsenic is arsenopyrite. Arsenic has an atomic number of 33 and a relative atomic mass of 74.91.

ARTERIOSCLEROSIS (är tîr´ē ō sklə rō´sĭs) Arteriosclerosis is a disease of the arteries, the main blood vessels that supply blood to the tissues of the body. The disease is often called "hardening of the arteries," because it involves hardening, thickening, and loss of elasticity in the artery walls.

There are several kinds of arteriosclerosis. For example, arteriolar sclerosis affects the body's small arteries, called the arterioles (see ARTERY; CIRCULATORY SYSTEM). The main form of arteriosclerosis is called atherosclerosis. It affects the medium and large arteries. Atherosclerosis has been found in people of all ages, though mostly in middle-aged and older people. The disease tends to develop over a period of years.

Atherosclerosis involves a buildup of fatty material on the inner walls of the arteries. Over time, these deposits enlarge and thicken to form plaques. The plaques, called atheromas, contain calcium, fatty acids, and cholesterol (see CHOLESTEROL). Atheromas have rough edges that scrape the smooth walls of the arteries. Scar tissue forms. The arteries become hard and narrow, decreasing the flow of blood. The roughened artery walls, together with the slower flow of blood through the arteries, can cause a blood clot to form. If such a clot occurs in an artery that supplies blood

to the heart and the artery becomes blocked, the person has a "heart attack." If such a clot occurs in the artery that supplies blood to the brain, a stroke may result (see HEART DISEASE; STROKE).

For various reasons, physicians do not know for certain how to prevent arteriosclerosis. For one thing, the disease seems to have no single cause. Also, some of the causes that contribute to the disease—called risk factors—include some that are not preventable. These unpreventable risk factors include a family tendency toward the disease, a person's sex (with males having a greater tendency toward the disease than females), and growing older.

However, some risk factors are preventable. One preventable risk factor is high blood cholesterol. A diet that is high in saturated fat (found in foods from animal sources, such as meat, eggs, and dairy products, as well as in tropical oils such as coconut oil) and in cholesterol (found only in foods from animal sources) will increase blood cholesterol in many people. Of these, saturated fat has the greater influence. Therefore, doctors recommend that people limit the amount of saturated fat and cholesterol in their diet. Where possible

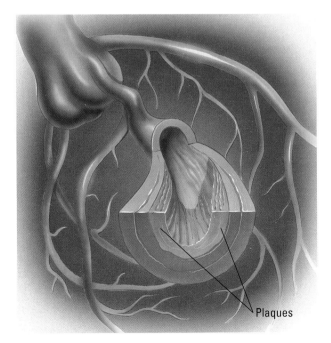

Plaques

ARTERIOSCLEROSIS

The illustration shows a cross section of an artery affected by atherosclerosis, the main form of arteriosclerosis. Notice the buildup of plaques and how they have narrowed the artery.

unsaturated fats, such as fish oils, corn, peanut, and soybean oils should be substituted for saturated fat in the diet. To help prevent arteriosclerosis, doctors also recommend that a person avoid smoking, get regular exercise, and keep his or her weight within normal limits.

To treat arteriosclerosis once it occurs, doctors also suggest reducing the risk factors. In addition, some patients may take drugs to lower the level of blood cholesterol.

In extreme cases, the diseased arteries can be removed and replaced with vessels from other parts of the body or with arteries made of synthetic materials. A less dangerous procedure, called angioplasty, involves inserting a deflated balloon into the artery and inflating it when it reaches the diseased area. This compresses the plaques and allows blood flow to return to normal.
See also ANGIOPLASTY.

ARTERY An artery is a blood vessel shaped like a tube with thick, elastic, muscular walls. Arteries carry blood away from the heart and to the lungs and the rest of the body (see CIRCULATORY SYSTEM). The main artery leaving the heart is the aorta, which carries bright, red, oxygen-rich blood (see AORTA). Smaller vessels branch off from the aorta and supply all the organs with blood. Blood returning to the heart contains too little oxygen to meet the body's needs. The pulmonary artery carries this blood to the lungs to pick up oxygen. As the heart pumps, a wave of pressure travels along the walls of the arteries and can be felt as a pulse through the skin over an artery. The smallest arteries are the arterioles. Their walls contract and relax and can regulate the amount of blood flowing to body tissues.

ARTESIAN WELL An artesian well is a hole drilled or dug down to underground water. In an artesian well, the water is trapped under great pressure between layers of rock. When the well is drilled, the pressure forces the water up through the hole.

Water can be trapped underground within a layer of porous rock called an aquifer (see

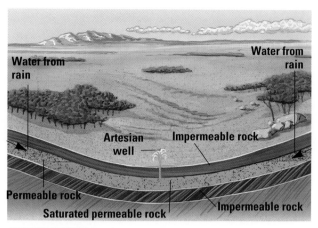

ARTESIAN WELL

An artesian well is a hole drilled or dug to underground water. In this diagram, the water is in a layer of permeable, or porous, rock between layers of impermeable, or solid, rock.

AQUIFER). Sometimes a natural opening allows water from an aquifer to stream out of the ground. This is called an artesian spring.

Some surface water of the Rocky Mountains seeps underground to an aquifer that is called the Dakota sandstone. This aquifer is part of a large geological formation called an artesian basin. Many artesian wells and artesian springs are usually found in an artesian basin. The largest artesian basin in the world is the Great Artesian Basin in Australia.
See also GROUNDWATER; WATER SUPPLY.

ARTHRITIS (är thrī'tĭs) Arthritis is a name for a group of diseases that cause joints in the body to be painful. The term *arthritis* comes from the Greek word meaning "joint inflammation."

People sometimes use the term *rheumatism* to mean arthritis. However, *rheumatism* is actually a more general term that refers to a variety of disorders of the muscles, joints, or connecting tissues, including arthritis.

Arthritis ranges in its severity. The disease can be a minor annoyance, or it can severely cripple a person. Single or multiple joints may be affected. Arthritic joints may become very swollen and crooked. Sometimes these joints become immovable. Although arthritis is more common in older people, it can occur in people of any age. The disease attacks twice as many women as it does men. It is not restricted to humans. The dinosaurs living in the Mesozoic era suffered from arthritis.

The exact cause of most kinds of arthritis is not known. Some kinds are caused by injuries or by abnormally high amounts of naturally occurring chemicals in the blood. Some kinds are caused by the wearing away of cartilage over a long life, with first symptoms occurring in old age, or by an allergic reaction to medicine (see ALLERGY). Some types of arthritis are thought to be caused by infection, most commonly by bacteria or viruses. Other types are thought to be due to the body's immune response to an unknown stimulus.

Scientists have recently discovered a new type of arthritis that is spread to humans by a bite from an infected tick. The disease has been named Lyme disease, after the town where it was discovered—Lyme, Connecticut (see TICK). Lyme arthritis is often signaled by a circular rash, which develops at the site of the tick bite.

Arthritis is usually treated with aspirin-type drugs to reduce pain and swelling. Other, stronger drugs, called steroids, are available to control severe pain and swelling for a short period of time. Some people who suffer from arthritis are helped by physical therapy (which includes vigorous body rubs, an exercise program, and sound waves transmitted into the body), supportive equipment, or surgery.

See also SKELETON.

ARTHROPODA (är thrŏp'ə də) Arthropoda is the largest phylum of the animal kingdom. It contains about eighty-five percent of all the

ARTHROPODA

Arthropods are widespread and varied in structure. This "family tree" presents the main groups of arthropods. Two extinct forms, the trilobites and the eurypterids, lived more than 400 million years ago. A living fossil arthropod is the horseshoe crab, which is not a crab, but is more closely related to the arachnids. The horseshoe crab has lived almost unchanged for 160 million years. The peripatus resembles the annelid worms, from which it evolved.

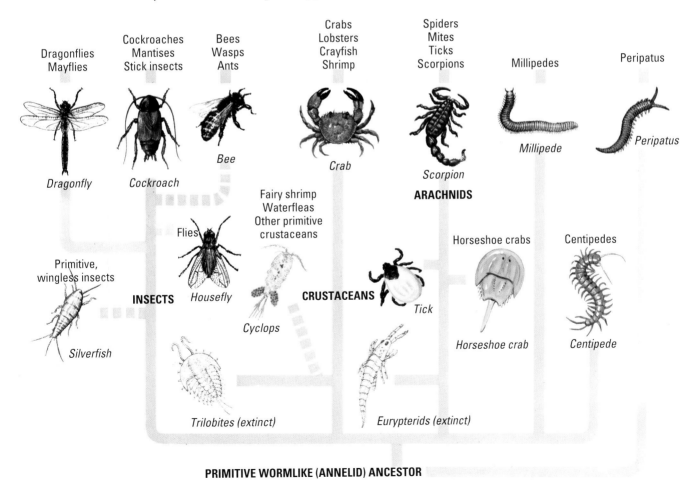

Dragonflies / Mayflies — Dragonfly

Cockroaches / Mantises / Stick insects — Cockroach

Bees / Wasps / Ants — Bee

Crabs / Lobsters / Crayfish / Shrimp — Crab

Spiders / Mites / Ticks / Scorpions — Scorpion — **ARACHNIDS**

Millipedes — Millipede

Peripatus — Peripatus

Primitive, wingless insects — Silverfish

INSECTS

Flies — Housefly

Fairy shrimp / Waterfleas / Other primitive crustaceans — Cyclops

CRUSTACEANS

Tick

Horseshoe crabs — Horseshoe crab

Centipedes — Centipede

Trilobites (extinct)

Eurypterids (extinct)

PRIMITIVE WORMLIKE (ANNELID) ANCESTOR

known animal species in the world. Insects, shrimp, spiders, and crabs all belong to Arthropoda.

All arthropods have jointed legs (see JOINT). *Arthropoda* comes from the Greek words meaning "jointed foot." Arthropods also have segmented bodies. Most species have a head, thorax, and abdomen. Arthropods do not have bones, but they do have a skeleton on the outside of their bodies. This is called an exoskeleton. It is made up of a hard material called chitin. The covering of a lobster or a cricket is an example of a chitin exoskeleton. The exoskeleton is also called the cuticle (see CHITIN; SKELETON).

Because the exoskeleton is hard and cannot expand, it prevents the animal from growing larger. Arthropods have developed a special way to grow. They shed their exoskeleton from time to time and form another, larger one. When an animal grows too large for the new exoskeleton, it will shed the exoskeleton and grow another. This process is called molting (see MOLTING).

The arthropods are the most highly evolved invertebrate animals. They probably had two common ancestors with the annelids (see ANNELIDA; INVERTEBRATE). Arthropods have the most complex nervous system of the invertebrates. They have antennae that are used for many things, such as touching, smelling, and hearing. Many arthropods have compound eyes. A compound eye is made up of hundreds of tiny eyes, each of which forms a separate image.

The Arthropoda phylum is divided into several classes (see CLASSIFICATION OF LIVING ORGANISMS). The major classes are Insecta (insects), Crustacea (crustaceans), Arachnida (spiders), Chilopoda (centipedes), and Diplopoda (millipedes).
See also ARACHNID; CRUSTACEAN; INSECT; MILLIPEDE.

ARTICHOKE Artichokes are plants belonging to the composite family (see COMPOSITE FAMILY). There are two kinds of plants called artichokes— the globe artichoke and the Jerusalem artichoke. The globe artichoke is native to the

ARTICHOKE
Globe artichokes are vegetable plants that have edible buds.

Mediterranean region. It is grown commercially in California. Its edible, unopened flower heads, or bud clusters, grow on stalks that are about 2 to 3 ft. [60 to 90 cm] high. The globe artichoke looks like a thistle. The Jerusalem artichoke is closely related to the sunflower. Its edible tubers, or swollen underground stems, look like potatoes. The Jerusalem artichoke grows to a height of 5 to 12 ft. [1.5 to 3.7 m].

ARTIFICIAL INSEMINATION Artificial insemination (AI) involves the injection of male sex cells (sperm), directly into the vagina or uterus (womb) of a female animal, without sexual intercourse taking place (see SEXUAL REPRODUCTION). AI is widely used in animal breeding to produce offspring with desired features found in the male that provided the sperm. These features can include rapid growth in either cattle or pigs. Since a sample of sperm can be split up, frozen, and transported to farms anywhere in the world, it is possible for more than 10,000 calves to be produced in one year from a single bull.

It is now possible for women to choose to be inseminated artificially if there is a medical problem that does not allow successful fertilization of her ovum (egg). The sperm of either the woman's usual partner or an anonymous donor (Artificial Insemination by Donor = AID) is injected by a syringe into the woman's vagina when one of her ovaries has produced an ovum. The timing of the insemination has to be exactly right to maximize the chance of fertilization.

There are now even sperm "banks" in several countries, where samples of donated human sperm are frozen in liquid nitrogen, ready for use at some future time.

ARTIFICIAL INTELLIGENCE

Artificial intelligence can be created by designing and programming a machine, especially a computer, so that it carries out tasks that require intelligence when carried out by humans. Scientists working on artificial intelligence have developed computer programs to solve problems. The programs can learn from their past mistakes and do not make them again. They get better at solving problems by learning from experience.

Artificial intelligence has been used in many fields. In medicine, computers have been programmed with information about many kinds of illnesses. Doctors can then diagnose a patient for those illnesses. In industry, computer-driven robots are used to assemble parts. Computers can also translate languages and even become expert chess players.

See also COMPUTER.

ARUM FAMILY

The arum family consists of about a thousand herbaceous plants, most of which are tropical. They are monocotyledons (see HERBACEOUS PLANT; MONOCOTYLEDON). Their leaves are shaped like swords. Most members of the arum family have brightly colored spathes (flowerlike parts) that are easily mistaken for flowers. Most of the species wind around or onto other plants (see EPIPHYTE). Some varieties found in swampy areas of North America include skunk cabbage, jack-in-the-pulpit, and elephant's ear.

Some of these plants give off a strong odor that attracts flies and other insects. The insect is then

ARUM FAMILY
One kind of arum plant is the jack-in-the-pulpit. The tiny flowers grow on a spike called a spadix, which is enfolded in a flowerlike hood called a spathe. Most species of arum are poisonous, but the roots may be made edible by cooking.

trapped by the spathes and the leaves. The movement of the insect trying to escape pollinates the plant (see POLLINATION).

Most plants in the arum family are poisonous. The poison can be removed by cooking. The light starchy paste left after boiling the roots is called arrowroot. It is used to thicken puddings and other desserts.

ASBESTOS

(ăs bĕs′təs) Asbestos is any one of several non-metallic minerals that may be separated into fibers. Chrysotile, the most widely used kind of asbestos, is found mainly in Canada and Russia (see MINERAL).

Asbestos was once used as insulation and in ceiling panels in schools and other public buildings throughout the United States. However, during the 1980s, much of the asbestos insulation and ceiling panels were removed because microscopic fibers in asbestos were thought to cause cancer. This practice is controversial because of the high costs associated with the removal of the asbestos. Nonetheless, governmental health agencies consider asbestos to be a hazardous waste capable of causing both cancer and lung disease. Strict public health laws are now in effect regarding its use, handling, and removal from buildings.

ASEPSIS

(ə sĕp′sĭs) Asepsis is the complete absence of any disease-causing microorganisms, commonly called germs. It is important for hospitals to provide an aseptic environment because microorganisms can enter cuts or wounds and cause infections. To ensure asepsis, disease-producing microorganisms are killed by sterilization (see STERILIZATION).

Operating rooms, surgical instruments, and other equipment are sterilized with steam, dry heat, or boiling water. The doctors and nurses wash with special antiseptics and wear sterile

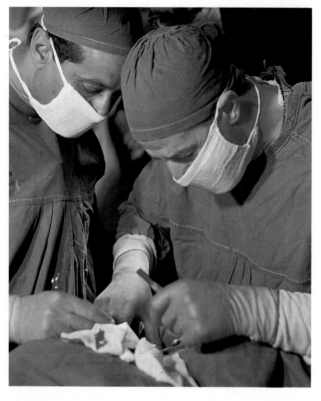

ASEPSIS
Every effort is made in hospitals to keep operating rooms free from microorganisms that can enter cuts or wounds and cause infections.

gowns, gloves, and face masks. The patient's skin is cleaned with an antiseptic before surgery (see ANTISEPTIC).

Aseptic technique has replaced the simple, less effective antiseptic methods used in the past. Asepsis has resulted in fewer infections after operations.

See also MICROORGANISM.

ASEXUAL REPRODUCTION (ā sĕk'shōō əl rē'prə dŭk'shən) Most organisms produce offspring by mating with a member of the opposite sex (see REPRODUCTION). Sometimes offspring can be produced without the help of a

member of the other sex. This is called asexual reproduction. There are many different types of asexual reproduction.

One-celled organisms, such as amebas, reproduce by binary fission. The original ameba simply splits in two. Before the split occurs, however, the ameba must split every part inside so that there are two of everything in the cell. When the cell splits, each half gets one of each part, so that the new amebas are identical.

Another type of asexual reproduction is budding. In many lower animals, such as the cnidarians, a new animal grows off of the side of another one. Then it breaks off and becomes a separate animal (see BUDDING).

Members of phylum Platyhelminthes can reproduce by regeneration. If a worm of the phylum breaks in half, each half grows back the missing piece. After a while, there are two whole worms.

In parthenogenesis, eggs are laid without being fertilized by a male (see FERTILIZATION; PARTHENOGENESIS). The offspring are identical to the mother.

Some lower plants produce spores asexually. Spores are similar to seeds, except that they are not produced by a female plant. They are produced by a plant without a sex. The spore may grow into a male or female plant, which can

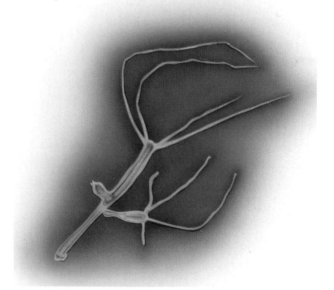

ASEXUAL REPRODUCTION
This freshwater polyp called hydra is showing asexual reproduction. A young individual is seen growing on the right, while an earlier stage is seen developing on the left.

engage in sexual reproduction and produce a plant that will again produce spores (see ALTERNATION OF GENERATIONS; SPORE).

Some of the higher plants, such as trees, can also reproduce asexually. If a branch of a willow tree breaks off and lands in water or moist soil, it can form roots and grow into another tree. This process is called vegetative propagation (see VEGETATIVE PROPAGATION).

All of the offspring produced by asexual reproduction are just like their parent. They are called clones (see CLONE). The more common sexual reproduction allows for change between parent and offspring. This change makes it possible for living things to adapt successfully to changing conditions.

If organisms reproduced only asexually, evolution would be nearly impossible.
See also ADAPTATION; EVOLUTION.

ASH Ash trees are hardwood, deciduous trees that grow in North America, Europe, and Asia (see DECIDUOUS TREE). They belong to the genus *Fraxinus*. They are members of the olive family. Sixteen species are native to the United States.

ASH
The ash tree is a member of the olive family.

The most common of these are the white ash, red ash, and black ash.

Ash trees may grow to more than 100 ft. [30 m] tall. Because ash is a strong hardwood, it is used in making baseball bats, oars, and the handles of shovels.

ASPARAGUS
The tender young green shoots, or spears, of asparagus are considered a delicacy.

ASPARAGUS (ə spăr′ə gəs) Asparagus is the name given to about 150 species of plants. Asparagus, which occurs naturally over a wide region from Siberia to southern Africa, is a member of the Liliaceae, or lily, family. Asparagus plants stand by themselves or can climb onto objects, such as fences or posts. Their roots give rise to unusual leaves, which look like small scales. Asparagus plants have small, greenish-yellow flowers in the spring, followed by small, red berries in the fall.

Asparagus can be grown in many kinds of soil. The best type of soil in which to grow asparagus year after year is a loose and light clay with a great deal of organic matter. Asparagus thrives in soil too salty for most crops. It does not grow well in soil containing large amounts of acid matter.

Three kinds of asparagus are sold as vegetables. Green spears and green spears with white stalks are the kinds produced for the fresh market. Asparagus is a good source of vitamin A.

A few types of asparagus, such as the *Asparagus plumosus*, are prized for their delicate leaves. They are used in corsages and in other plant arrangements.

ASPARTAME (ăs′pər tām′) Aspartame is a synthetic, or human-made, food sweetener. Aspartame is many times sweeter than sugar, so a lesser amount is used. This results in fewer calories than if sugar were used to sweeten food. Aspartame has many uses. For example, aspartame is used in diet soft drinks and diet foods, and as a sugar substitute in coffee and tea. Aspartame largely replaced saccharine and other artificial sweeteners. Aspartame is sold under the trade names *NutraSweet* and *Equal*.
See also SUGAR.

ASPHALT Asphalt is a black or brown mineral material used in making roads and in waterproofing roofs, water tanks, and boats. It is also used as an adhesive. Asphalt consists of hydrocarbons combined with nitrogen, sulfur, and oxygen (see HYDROCARBON). It can be obtained from natural deposits, called asphaltum, or from the distillation of crude petroleum (see DISTILLATION). Large deposits of natural asphalt occur in Texas, Oklahoma, Utah, and California. The world's largest deposits are found in western Canada. Venezuela, Cuba, and the Philippines also have asphalt deposits.

Asphalt becomes a heavy liquid when heated. To make road surfaces, the hot liquid is mixed with crushed stone. The mixture is then spread and rolled.

Asphalt is an ancient building material, used by the Babylonians and mentioned in the Bible. It was used to seal the walls of a reservoir in Pakistan in 3,000 B.C.

ASPIRIN Aspirin, or acetylsalicylic acid, is a white, powdered analgesic. An analgesic is a substance that reduces or stops pain without causing unconsciousness or complete loss of feeling. Besides being an analgesic, aspirin reduces inflammation and fever. It is used to treat symptoms of arthritis, colds, and influenza (flu), as well as headaches and other body pains. Aspirin also has been found effective in keeping clots from forming in the blood. Some research suggests that aspirin may be useful in preventing strokes (see STROKE). Aspirin is mildly acidic and may irritate some people's stomachs. Manufacturers often add sodium bicarbonate, a form of salt, to make aspirin less acidic. Doctors may also recommend acetaminophen, a less irritating analgesic. Aspirin usually is sold in the form of pills or caplets.
See also ANALGESIC.

ASS The ass is a relative of the horse. It looks like a zebra without stripes. Its height to the top of its shoulder is 3 to 5 ft. [90 to 150 cm]. It can run very swiftly. It has long ears and is usually gray with a dark brown or black mane.

Wild asses live on the hot, dry plains of Africa and Asia. The onager is a wild ass of Africa. The kulan, the kiang, and the ghorkhar are wild asses of Asia. Because they are hunted for their hides and their meat, wild asses are in danger of becoming extinct.

The African wild ass is the ancestor of the donkey.

ASPHALT
One of the most important uses of asphalt is in surfacing roads.

ASS

Wild asses are in danger of becoming extinct because they are hunted for their hides and for their meat.

Thousands of years ago, humans captured the wild asses of Africa. By training these animals to do work, people developed a domesticated animal that was given the name *donkey*. Today there are many varieties of donkeys.

See also DONKEY.

ASSAYING (ăs'ā'ĭng) In science, assaying is a method used to find out how much and what kinds of metals are in a rock or an unknown alloy (see ALLOY). At one time, assaying was concerned only with finding out how much gold or silver was in an alloy.

Assays are carried out by using various means of chemical analysis. The main methods of assaying are the wet process and the dry process. In the wet process, the unknown sample is mixed with other chemicals in solution (see SOLUTION AND SOLUBILITY). The resulting products are separated and weighed. During the dry process, the sample may be crushed and pure substances sifted out.

ASTER The aster is a flowering perennial plant of the composite family. There are more than two hundred known varieties in North America. The flower of this herbaceous plant is shaped like a disk (see COMPOSITE FAMILY; HERBACEOUS PLANT; PERENNIAL PLANT). It has many thin, pointed petals, which give it a starlike appearance. Its colors range from white to pink to deep blue and purple.

The aster blooms in late summer. In some warmer areas, the flowers may last until early winter. Although some asters may grow from seeds, reproduction is usually by vegetative propagation (see VEGETATIVE PROPAGATION). Relatives of the aster include the chrysanthemum and the sunflower.

ASTER

There are more than two hundred varieties of asters in North America. Their many-petaled disk-shaped flowers range in color from white to deep purple.

ASTEROID An asteroid is a minor planet that orbits the sun. Most asteroids travel in space between the orbits of Mars and Jupiter in a region known as the asteroid belt. Asteroids are much smaller than major planets. Some asteroids are only about 1 mi. [1.5 km] in diameter. Ceres, the largest asteroid, has a diameter of 596 mi. [959 km]. It is nearly spherical in shape. There are

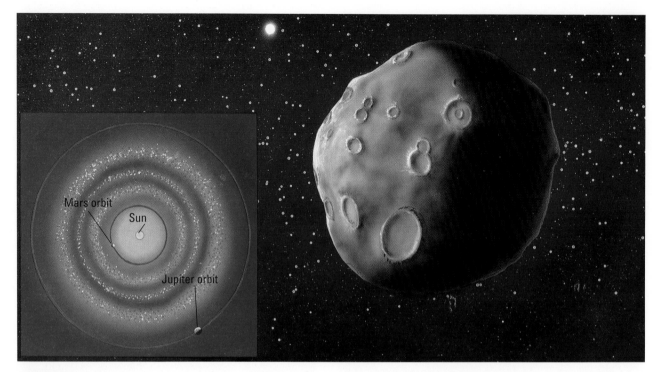

ASTEROID

The main illustration shows a closeup of an asteroid. The bright star in the distance is Jupiter. The asteroid belt lies between the orbits of Jupiter and Mars (see inset). There are gaps in the asteroid belt, where no asteroids are found. These are called Kirkwood gaps.

about 100,000 asteroids. The majority of them are too small to be seen from Earth. Only one, Vesta, can be seen without a telescope.

Eros is a small asteroid that wanders from the asteroid belt and comes close to the earth, within 16 million mi. [25.6 million km]. Scientists observe the movement of Eros to determine the astronomical unit, the distance between the earth and the sun.

See also ASTRONOMICAL UNIT.

ASTHMA (ăz′mə) Asthma is a very common disease that causes a person to feel short of breath or to have other problems with breathing. When a person with asthma, called an asthmatic, has an asthma attack, he or she may have difficulty breathing, causing him or her to gasp and wheeze. A feeling of tightness in the chest and a chronic (long lasting or recurring) cough also may be signs of asthma. Asthma attacks often occur at night, after heavy exercise, after prolonged exposure to cold air or irritating fumes, or when a person is emotionally upset. A viral infection of the nose and throat may possibly trigger an asthma attack.

In an asthma attack, the bronchial tubes of the lungs narrow (see LUNG). This may occur because of a tightening of the muscles around the bronchial tubes or because of a swelling of the membranes that line the tubes and increased production of mucus by these membranes. The flow of air through the tubes is then partially blocked, resulting in the symptoms described above. Asthma is commonly caused by allergy to dust, pollen, animal fur, or certain foods. Asthma is often linked with hay fever, another kind of allergy (see ALLERGY).

A doctor identifies asthma by doing a physical exam. He or she may use tests of lung function, a chest X-ray, allergy skin tests, or blood tests to determine which substances a person is allergic to and what the best treatment of the disease is. Treatment depends on the severity of the symptoms. During a severe asthma attack, the patient must go to a hospital emergency room, where he or she may be given oxygen and drugs to control the symptoms. For less severe asthma, the doctor may prescribe any of various drugs in the form of an aerosol inhaler, which the patient uses during waking hours to keep the bronchial tubes wide open. Patients with very severe asthma may need to take drugs called steroids daily.

ASTROLABE (ăs′ trə lāb′)

An astrolabe is an instrument once used by astronomers and ships' navigators to measure the altitude of the stars and planets. There were two kinds: astronomical astrolabes and sea astrolabes. The earliest known astronomical astrolabes were made in Syria in the ninth century, though they may have been invented by the Greeks. An astronomical astrolabe was modeled on the movement of the sky. On a circular base-plate, circles were engraved representing imaginary circles in the sky (see CELESTIAL SPHERE). An intricately shaped metal piece, called a rete (rē′ tē) (meaning a network), rotated over the circular base-plate. It represented the positions of the brightest fixed stars.

ASTROLABE

This is an astronomical astrolabe made in the 14th century. The altitude, or height, of a star in degrees above the horizon could be found by sighting it along the "needle" pivoted at the center.

The user would measure the altitude, or height, of a star or the sun above the horizon in degrees, minutes, and seconds, using a sight attached to the astrolabe (see MEASUREMENT). It showed the latitude, or distance north or south of the equator, of the user (see LATITUDE AND LONGITUDE). The user could then turn the rete until it represented the position of this star and read off the time of day from the astrolabe.

The sea astrolabe came into use in the fifteenth century. It simply had a sight attached to a circular scale and was used for measuring the altitude of the sun or stars.

Today, sea navigators use an instrument called a sextant to obtain the altitudes of heavenly bodies. The sextant is a highly improved version of the sea astrolabe.

See also NAVIGATION; QUADRANT.

ASTROLOGY (ə strŏl′ə jē)

Astrology is an unscientific approach to predicting what will happen in a person's life by studying the moon, the sun, the planets, and the stars. Astrology is based on a belief that these heavenly bodies influence human affairs. Astrology is also based on the belief that a person will have particular characteristics depending on what position the heavenly bodies were in when he or she was born.

Astrology began more than three thousand years ago in Babylonia. It was the beginning of the science of astronomy, which is the scientific study of the heavenly bodies, including their motions, size, and composition (see ASTRONOMY). The astrology of ancient Egypt identified 12 signs of the zodiac that are named after constellations. People who practice astrology use the zodiac in their predictions. These people are called astrologers. Even though most scientists believe modern astrology has no scientific basis, many people still believe in it.

See also CONSTELLATION; ZODIAC.

ASTROLOGY

Behind astrology lies the belief that the heavenly bodies influence our lives. Astrologers describe the positions of the sun and planets in relation to the 12 constellations of the zodiac, through which they move. These are represented by the 12 signs shown around the circle below.

ASTRONAUTICS (ăs´ trə nô´tĭks) Astronautics is the science of flight in space beyond the earth's atmosphere. It applies knowledge gained from various sciences to the design, construction, and operation of spacecraft. Astronautics deals with ways to control and track the flight of spacecraft. It also deals with the unusual conditions (such as weightlessness) that crews experience during spaceflight (see GRAVITY; WEIGHTLESSNESS).

Astronautics is a relatively recent science. It had its beginnings in the science of aeronautics, which deals with flight within the earth's atmosphere. Because vehicles designed for spaceflight also have to be able to operate within the earth's atmosphere (during launch and reentry), astronautics and aeronautics are overlapping sciences (see AERONAUTICS). Astronautics deals mainly with ways to use jet propulsion to control the direction and speed of a spacecraft outside a planet's atmosphere (see JET PROPULSION).

The first recorded use of the word *astronautics* was in 1927. The development of a distinct science of spaceflight occurred rapidly after the Soviet Union launched the first two *Sputnik* satellites in 1957. In July 1969, the United States successfully sent two astronauts, in the spacecraft *Apollo 11*, to the moon. By 1975, more than a

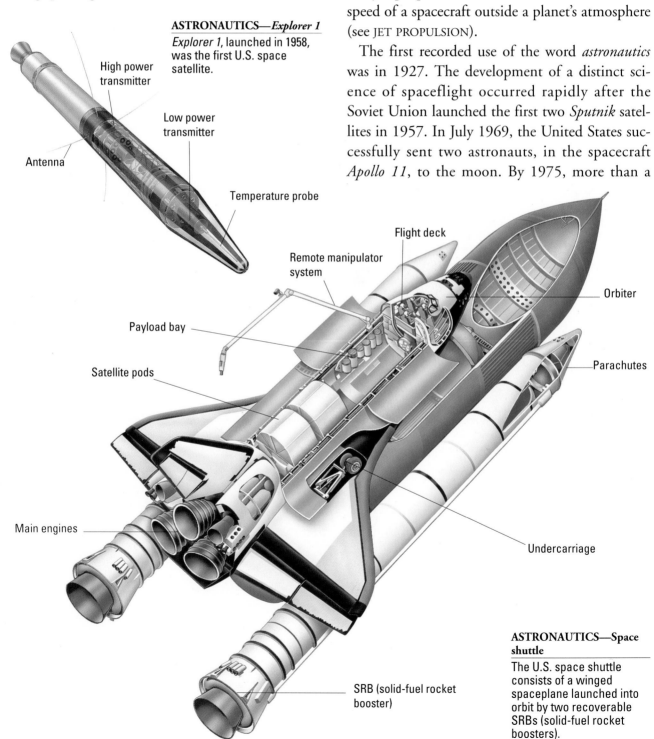

ASTRONAUTICS—*Explorer 1*
Explorer 1, launched in 1958, was the first U.S. space satellite.

High power transmitter

Low power transmitter

Antenna

Temperature probe

Flight deck

Remote manipulator system

Payload bay

Orbiter

Satellite pods

Parachutes

Main engines

Undercarriage

SRB (solid-fuel rocket booster)

ASTRONAUTICS—Space shuttle
The U.S. space shuttle consists of a winged spaceplane launched into orbit by two recoverable SRBs (solid-fuel rocket boosters).

hundred space missions had been successfully flown, including seven moon landings (see APOLLO PROJECT). The first reusable manned spacecraft—the space shuttle *Columbia*—was successfully tested by the United States in 1981. Many space shuttle flights have been made since then.

As astronautics rapidly became a fully developed science, the purposes of each new spaceflight became more ambitious. Spacecraft have been fitted with many kinds of instruments for gathering information about the environment of space. All of the moon's surface has been mapped in great detail by both manned and unmanned spacecraft. Television cameras in unmanned spacecraft have taken closeup pictures of Mars, Jupiter, and all the other planets in our solar system except Pluto. Various kinds of scientific detectors mounted on space probes send back to Earth information about the weather, temperature, and biological conditions.

These probes can be controlled by radio. Their flight path can be changed, their cameras aimed, and their equipment turned on and off.

Astronautics has developed satellites whose purposes include military reconnaissance, long-distance communications, radiation measurement, and astronomical observation. Some of these satellites remain in constant orbit. Navigation satellites send radio signals that can help a ship at sea check its course. Communications satellites make it possible to send live television pictures over very long distances (see SATELLITE).

Astronautics has provided much new information for astronomers. Satellites can take photographs of the sun and planets without the distortion that occurs when the photographs are taken from Earth. Unmanned satellites equipped with scientific detectors can obtain information that cannot yet be obtained by manned spacecraft.

ASTRONAUTICS—Satellites

Earth resources satellites (right) circle the earth in low orbits, mapping the surface and identifying mineral deposits by the color of the reflected light.

ASTRONAUTICS—*Voyager 2*

Voyager 2 (below) was launched in 1977 on a journey through the outer solar system to study the giant planets.

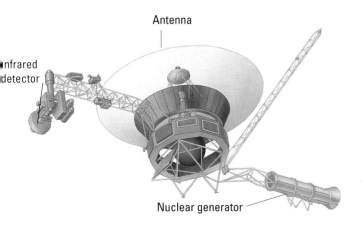

Antenna

Infrared detector

Nuclear generator

Astronautics will eventually make it possible to establish a base on the moon, orbit a permanent space station, and send an expedition to Mars. *See also* SPACE EXPLORATION.

ASTRONOMICAL UNIT The astronomical unit is used by astronomers and astrophysicists to measure distances in outer space. It is approximately equal to 93,000,000 mi. [149,600,000 km], the mean distance between the earth and the sun.
See also LIGHT-YEAR; PARSEC.

Astronomy (ə strŏn'ə mē) is the scientific study of the stars, planets, and other things that make up the universe. Scientists who work in the field of astronomy are called astronomers. They study celestial (heavenly) bodies with telescopes, radar, spectroscopes, cameras, artificial satellites, and spacecraft. Astronomers gather information about everything outside of the earth's atmosphere. They also provide information for navigation and for the measurement of time on Earth.

Ancient roots of astronomy Astronomy is thousands of years old. It has its roots in astrology, the study of heavenly bodies to discover their supposed influence on human life (see ASTROLOGY). In ancient Babylonia, the sun, the moon, and the stars were studied both for astrological reasons and to establish a calendar. In ancient Egypt, when certain stars appeared at certain locations, the people knew that it was time for the Nile River to flood. For example, the appearance of the constellation Aquarius was a warning. It meant that preparations for the flood should begin (see CONSTELLATION; ZODIAC). In North and South America, the Mayan and Incan civilizations based their architecture on astronomical observations.

Astronomy flourished in ancient Greece. About 2,500 years ago, Pythagoras knew that the earth was a sphere, though he believed it was at the center of the universe. Around 270 B.C., Aristarchus suggested that the earth moves around the sun.

But in about A.D. 127, another Greek scholar, Ptolemy, wrote a book that was to be the basis of astronomy for the next 1,400 years. Like almost all of the early astronomers, he believed that the

OBSERVATORY

The William Herschel telescope on La Palma, Canary Islands, is a reflecting telescope. It has a mirror 165 in. [4.2 m] across, and is the third largest in the world. The telescope came into use in 1987. It is operated by Britain's Royal Greenwich Observatory. The observatory is built on top of a mountain 8,000 ft. [2,400 m] tall. The telescope can be aimed at any part of the sky through wide slits in the large dome that surrounds it.

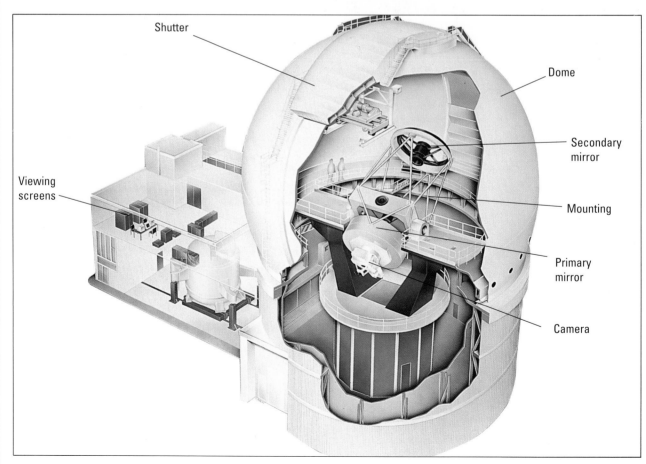

Shutter · Dome · Secondary mirror · Mounting · Primary mirror · Camera · Viewing screens

LARGEST TELESCOPE
The world's largest telescope was built in 1992 on top of Mount Kea, Hawaii. Called the Keck telescope, it has a mirror 32.5 ft. [10 m] across, made up of 36 smaller mirrors fitted together.

earth was at the center of the universe. He thought that the sun, moon, stars, and planets revolved around Earth, which did not move at all.

Beginnings of modern astronomy

Modern astronomy began with the work of Nicolaus Copernicus, in the 1500s (see COPERNI-CUS). In 1543, the year of his death, he published a book in which he repeated the suggestion of Aristarchus that the earth moved around the sun. Copernicus explained that the earth was a planet and that all planets orbited the sun, contradicting Ptolemy's idea of the universe.

Later, Tycho Brahe, of Denmark, spent many years studying the stars and the planets (see BRAHE, TYCHO). He kept careful records of the positions of the stars and planets. Brahe died before he was able to complete his work. Another astronomer, Johannes Kepler, used Brahe's work to discover how planets moved around the sun (see KEPLER, JOHANNES). Kepler was a mathematician. He was able to show that each of the planets traveled in an elliptical orbit around the sun. An elliptical orbit is one that is shaped like a flattened circle (see ELLIPSE).

Galileo and Newton At the same time that Kepler was calculating the orbits of the planets, Galileo was developing the telescope (see GALILEO; TELESCOPE). This instrument enabled humans to see the sky better than ever before. In 1610, Galileo observed the moons of Jupiter and the moonlike phases of Venus. After Galileo's death in 1642, the English astronomer and mathematician Sir Isaac Newton made the most important discoveries since the time of Copernicus (see NEWTON, SIR ISAAC). Newton's three laws of mechanics and his law of gravitation explained the movements of all heavenly bodies. He proved, for example, that gravitation controls the orbit of the moon. Newton's study of the colors in sunlight led to the invention of the spectroscope, which was to become a valuable tool for astronomers (see SPECTROSCOPE).

Discovery of the planets Using the discoveries of Copernicus, Brahe, Kepler, Newton, and others, astronomers later located planets that had never before been found. In 1781, Sir William Herschel discovered Uranus (see HERSCHEL, SIR WILLIAM). Neptune was discovered by J. G. Galle

in 1846 after its existence had been predicted by Urbain Leverrier and John Couch Adams, working independently. Early in the 1900s, Sir Percival Lowell predicted the existence of Pluto (see LOWELL, PERCIVAL). In 1930, the planet was sighted by astronomers at Lowell Observatory in Flagstaff, Arizona. Pluto was the ninth principal planet of the solar system to be discovered. Five of the nine planets had been known since ancient times (see PLANET; SOLAR SYSTEM). Ceres was the first asteroid (minor planet) to be discovered. It was found by astronomers in 1801. Today over 3,500 asteroids are known, and scientists continue to find them (see ASTEROID).

Stars While some astronomers searched for planets, other astronomers searched for stars. In the early 1800s, Joseph Fraunhofer became one of the first astronomers to use the spectroscope to examine starlight. His work led to a new branch of astronomy called astrophysics (see ASTROPHYSICS).

Photography Photography is an important tool of astronomy. In 1840, astronomers first photographed the moon. By 1850, photographs of the stars had become possible. Today, astronomers use cameras that are very complex and sensitive. These cameras are able to photograph stars that cannot be seen by the eye, even with a telescope. In the United States, astronomers at Harvard

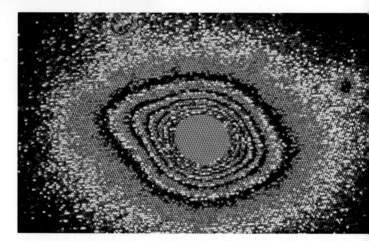

University have been adding information to a catalog of stars since 1885. It is called the *Henry Draper Catalogue.* It contains photographs and measurements of more than 400,000 stars.

Meteorites, meteoroids, and comets

Astronomers also study meteorites, meteoroids, and comets. Meteoroids are particles of rock, most of them the size of dust grains, that orbit the sun. If one falls into the earth's atmosphere, it becomes intensely hot because of friction with the air and burns up. We see it as a meteor, or shooting star (see METEOR). Very large meteoroids, the size of a fist or larger, reach the ground before they burn up. The fragments are called meteorites. Some weigh more than a ton. In Arizona, there is a crater 4,000 ft. [1,210 m] across and 600 ft. [183 m] deep that was caused by a meteor's impact.

Comets are masses of rock, ice, and frozen substances including carbon dioxide, methane, and ammonia (see COMET). They are normally too dark to see with the naked eye. When they approach the sun, the icy materials turn into gas, and the comet develops a long glowing tail. For several months the comet can be seen slowly moving across the sky. At intervals of millions of years, comets may also strike the earth.

Telescopes Telescopes are the instruments most often used by astronomers. With one of the largest reflecting telescopes in the world, astronomers at the Palomar Observatory in California are able to photograph stars that are a billion light-years away. One of the world's largest refracting telescopes is at Yerkes Observatory in Wisconsin. Radio telescopes are used to receive and record radio waves that are sent out by objects in space. In the 1960s, astronomers discovered new kinds of objects in space by using radio astronomy (see PULSAR; QUASAR). In 1965, astronomers used radar to learn how long it takes for Mercury and Venus to rotate (spin) (see RADIO ASTRONOMY).

PUBLIC ASTRONOMY
In San Francisco, California, people stand in line to look through a telescope.

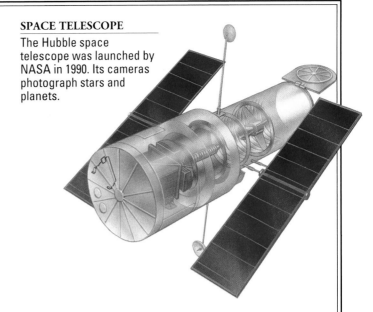

SPACE TELESCOPE
The Hubble space telescope was launched by NASA in 1990. Its cameras photograph stars and planets.

Recent developments The space technology of the twentieth century has led to great advances in astronomy. One of the most important advances has been the regular use of space probes and artificial satellites (see SATELLITE; SPACE EXPLORATION). In 1947, the United States launched a rocket to take the first photographs outside the atmosphere. In 1959, a space probe launched by the Soviet Union televised the first pictures of the side of the moon that is always turned away from Earth. In the 1960s, astronauts left astronomical equipment on the moon, and space probes landed on Venus and Mars. During the *Skylab* missions of the 1970s, the cloud-covered surface of Venus was mapped in great detail. Two *Voyager* spacecraft sent back spectacular photos of Jupiter and its moons (1979), Saturn (1980-1981), Uranus (1986), and Neptune (1989) as the probes flew by each planet. Several probes were launched by different nations in 1985 to view Halley's comet in early 1986. The *Magellan* space probe was launched in 1989. It went into orbit around Venus in 1990 and photographed the planet's surface. This provided the first complete map of the surface of Venus. The *Galileo* probe was launched towards Jupiter in 1989, and by chance was well placed to observe the collision of Comet Shoemaker–Levy 9 with the giant planet in 1994. New space probes and satellites continue to be launched and to extend our knowledge of the earth and the solar system.

ASTROPHYSICS (ăs′trō fĭz′ĭks) Astrophysics is the study of the physical and chemical makeup of celestial, or heavenly, bodies. It applies the theories and methods of physics to determine the structure of stars and to solve some of the mysteries of astronomy (see PHYSICS).

Astrophysics is largely an observational science. It includes the study of the kinds of energy given off by the sun and the other stars, as well as by planets and nebulae (large clouds of gases and dust). It is particularly concerned with the study of the electromagnetic radiation given off by the bodies (see ELECTROMAGNETIC RADIATION).

Most of the electromagnetic energy given out by stars is blocked by the earth's atmosphere. Only visible light waves, radio waves, and some ultraviolet and infrared radiation pass through the atmosphere and reach the earth's surface.

Astrophysics began by studying the visible light given out by stars. By analyzing this starlight, an astrophysicist can determine which elements are present inside the star. Starlight is collected by a telescope and analyzed by an instrument called a spectroscope. The spectroscope spreads the light out into all the colors that it contains. This is called a rainbow spectrum. The star's rainbow spectrum is crossed by dark lines where some of the colors are missing. They are absent because they have been filtered out by the star's own atmosphere. Because scientists know which elements filter out certain wavelengths of light, they can calculate the elements the star contains. The brightness of the colors that are visible give scientists clues as to how hot the star is (see SPECTROSCOPE).

In the 1930s, when radio signals from space were discovered, astrophysicists started using radio telescopes to study them (see RADIO ASTRONOMY). The development of rockets and artificial satellites in the 1950s made it possible to lift telescopes and radiation detectors above the earth's atmosphere. In space, they can detect the whole range of wavelengths of radiation given out by stars and galaxies. These include gamma rays, X rays, ultraviolet rays, and infrared rays. The presence and intensity of radiation at these different wavelengths provide evidence for the nuclear and chemical reactions occurring inside stars, galaxies, and nebulae. Astrophysics also deals with determining the distances between stars and the motions of the stars, as well as the orbits of planets and their natural satellites (see SATELLITE). These studies help astrophysicists to make maps of the galaxies.

Astrophysicists try to explain the fantastic discoveries of astronomers, such as black holes, pulsars, and quasars (see BLACK HOLE; PULSAR; QUASAR). Astrophysicists are giving close attention to quasars, for instance, because quasars are the most distant objects detectable from the earth. A quasar is faint blue in color when viewed through a telescope. Study of the light of quasars indicates that they are moving away from the earth's galaxy (the Milky Way) at very high speeds. The fastest are traveling at nearly the speed of light (see RED SHIFT). The brightness of a quasar can be more than that of a hundred galaxies combined. But they are so far from Earth that they seem like faint stars, far too dim to be seen with the naked eye.

One of the difficulties in studying very distant heavenly bodies is that only evidence that existed in the past can be observed. Scientists cannot directly determine anything about the present state of even the closest stars and other celestial objects. That is because light or radio waves—from which scientists get nearly all their evidence about heavenly bodies—take so long to reach Earth. Light from the sun, for example, takes about eight minutes to reach the earth. Light from nearby stars takes a few years to reach us, but from others it takes thousands of years. Light reaching the earth from quasars was emitted billions of years ago.

The light emitted by a star can give the astrophysicist information about its surface. However, what the inside of a star is like must be inferred, using the sciences of physics and chemistry. For example, if the surface temperature of a star is 5,000 degrees, the inside temperature will be millions of degrees. By taking into account a star's weight, mass, surface temperature, and light, an astrophysicist can calculate its approximate age and may even be able to trace its probable history. *See also* ASTRONOMY; COSMOLOGY; GALAXY; SOLAR SYSTEM.

ATMOSPHERE

The atmosphere is the mass of gases that surrounds the earth. It is about 500 mi. [800 km] high. Its total weight is about 5.6 million billion tons [5.1 million billion metric tons].

The force of gravity holds the earth's atmosphere around the earth. Other planets in our solar system also have a gravitational force strong enough to hold an atmosphere in place (see GRAVITY). However, their atmospheres are different from the one that surrounds Earth. Two gases, nitrogen and oxygen, make up 99 percent of the volume of the earth's atmosphere.

Air is necessary to life (see AIR). Animals and most plants breathe the oxygen in it. The atmosphere protects the earth from harm. It prevents harmful ultraviolet rays from reaching the earth by acting as a filter between the earth and the sun. Acting as a blanket, the atmosphere keeps the earth from losing too much heat at night. It also protects the earth from most meteors and cosmic rays (see COSMIC RAYS; METEOR).

If you were to fly up through the atmosphere, studying it with measuring instruments, you would find that it changed as you got higher and farther away from Earth. The higher you went, the thinner the air would get, because the molecules of its gases are farther apart. The air is so thin above 25,000 ft. [7,600 m] that travelers must have extra oxygen to survive.

To help describe the differences among the levels of the atmosphere, scientists have divided it into four layers. Starting with the layer next to the earth's surface, they are the troposphere, the stratosphere, the ionosphere, and the exosphere. Within the stratosphere lies the ozone layer. The ozone layer absorbs much of the sun's harmful ultraviolet rays (see OZONE).

Troposphere About 75 percent of the entire mass of the atmosphere is in the troposphere.

RED SKY

The red sky in this sunset is caused by particles of dust in the atmosphere. Blue light is scattered by dust, but the red light passes through.

141

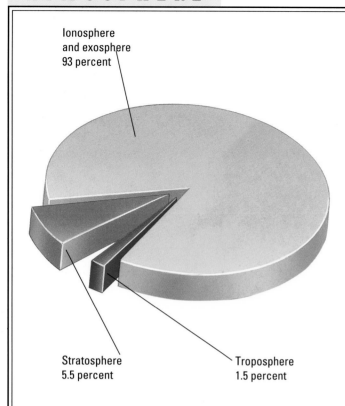

Ionosphere
and exosphere
93 percent

Stratosphere
5.5 percent

Troposphere
1.5 percent

COMPOSITION OF THE ATMOSPHERE BY VOLUME

The diagram above shows that the troposphere (the layer closest to the earth) occupies the smallest volume. The ionosphere and exosphere occupy the greatest volume.

It starts at the earth's surface and extends outward to an altitude (height) of 5 to 10 mi. [8 to 16 km]. It is the layer in which all of the earth's weather occurs.

The air in the troposphere is about 80 percent nitrogen and about 20 percent oxygen. It contains tiny amounts of the unreactive gas argon and even less of carbon dioxide. Most of the water and dust that is present in the atmosphere is also found in this layer.

About 45 percent of the sun's radiation reaching the earth is absorbed by the ground; 18 percent is absorbed by the atmosphere; and 37 percent is reflected back into space. Most of the 18 percent absorbed by the atmosphere is absorbed by the carbon dioxide, water vapor, and dust in the

LAYERS OF THE ATMOSPHERE

A cross section of the earth's atmosphere shows the main layers and their average temperature. The earth's atmosphere is a shallow layer of gases held to the planet by gravity. It shields the earth's surface from ultraviolet radiation and keeps the temperature at a level at which liquid water can exist. Plants replenish the atmosphere's oxygen, on which all living things depend.

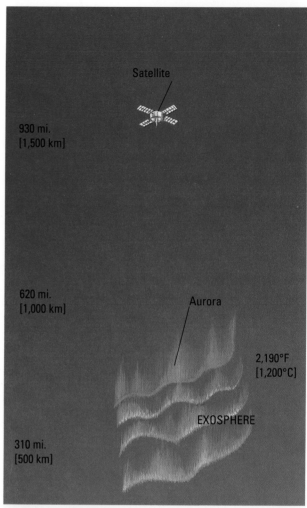

Satellite

930 mi.
[1,500 km]

620 mi.
[1,000 km]

Aurora

2,190°F
[1,200°C]

EXOSPHERE

310 mi.
[500 km]

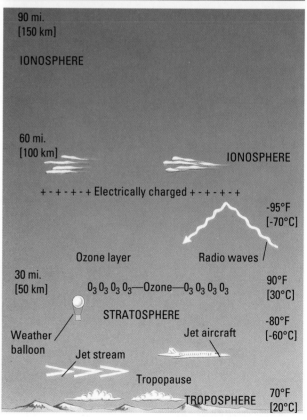

90 mi.
[150 km]

IONOSPHERE

60 mi.
[100 km]

IONOSPHERE

+ - + - + - + Electrically charged + - + - + - +

-95°F
[-70°C]

Ozone layer

Radio waves

30 mi.
[50 km]

O₃ O₃ O₃ O₃—Ozone—O₃ O₃ O₃ O₃

90°F
[30°C]

STRATOSPHERE

-80°F
[-60°C]

Weather
balloon

Jet aircraft

Jet stream

Tropopause

TROPOSPHERE

70°F
[20°C]

These are narrow and fast-moving currents of air called jet streams (see JET STREAM). In and beyond the upper troposphere, the atmosphere contains too little oxygen to support life.

The uppermost limit of the troposphere is called the tropopause. Its altitude varies from 5 mi. [8 km] in some places to 11 mi. [18 km]. Its temperature also varies, from -60°F [-51°C] at the lowest altitudes to -110°F [-79°C] at the highest.

Stratosphere Above the equator, the stratosphere begins at a height of 10 mi. [16 km] and extends to a height of 50 mi. [80 km]. Closer to the poles, the stratosphere begins closer to the ground. Its composition is very similar to that of the troposphere. There are only a few clouds in the stratosphere. They are made up mostly of ice crystals. These crystals form on the small particles of dust that remain when meteoroids burn up in the atmosphere. The only winds in the stratosphere are jet streams and other fast-moving winds. Jet streams blow toward the east. Because they help planes fly faster and save fuel, eastward-bound pilots like to fly in them on long trips.

Jet pilots also prefer to fly in the stratosphere to avoid the storms that occur in the troposphere below. Airplanes flying in the stratosphere may leave behind trails like long, thin, white clouds. These are called contrails, which is short for "condensation trails." They are made up of freezing water from a plane's exhaust.

In the upper part of the stratosphere, the temperature rises with increasing height. This is because the ozone there absorbs the energy of the ultraviolet light from the sun. Because it controls the amount of ultraviolet light that reaches the earth, the ozone layer is very important. Scientists are concerned about its possible destruction by the exhaust of supersonic jets and by chlorofluorocarbons used on Earth (see CHLOROFLUORO-CARBON; OZONE).

Ionosphere The ionosphere begins at an altitude of 50 mi. [80 km] and ends about 300 mi. [480 km] above the earth. It is called the

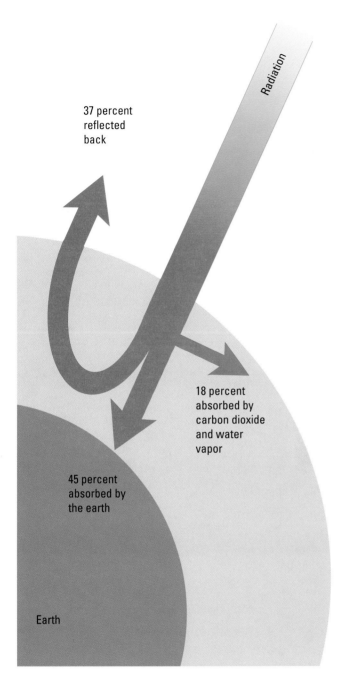

37 percent reflected back

Radiation

18 percent absorbed by carbon dioxide and water vapor

45 percent absorbed by the earth

Earth

THE ATMOSPHERE AND SUN'S RADIATION
The sun's radiation is a mixture of visible light, heat rays, and ultraviolet rays. About 37 percent of the radiation reaching the earth is reflected back. About 45 percent is absorbed by the earth, and about 18 percent is absorbed by clouds, dust, and carbon dioxide in the atmosphere.

troposphere. The carbon dioxide, water vapor, and dust are thicker near the ground. This is why the warmest temperatures in the troposphere are to be found near the earth. As the height of the troposphere increases, its temperature drops at the rate of 20°F per mi. [7°C per km].

In the upper troposphere, strong winds blow.

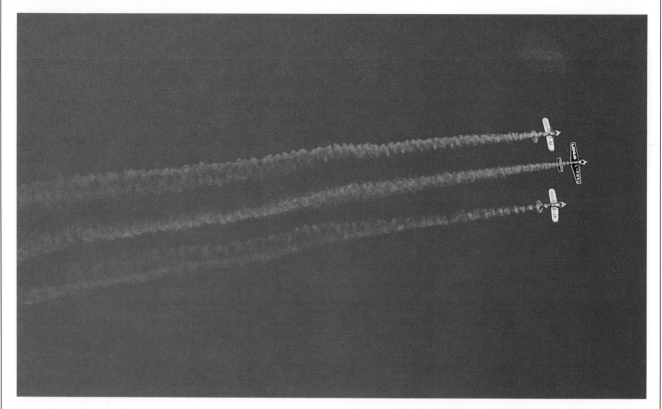

ARTIFICIAL CLOUDS

"Contrails" stream from three planes. They consist of water droplets condensing as the moist exhaust gases from the planes' engines cool and can no longer hold as much water vapor. The droplets form artificial clouds that can linger for hours. Real clouds consist of water droplets or ice crystals that condense when warm, moisture-laden air rises and cools.

ionosphere because the sun's radiation ionizes most of the molecules in its thin air (see IONS AND IONIZATION). The ionosphere is important in radio astronomy and in communications with artificial satellites. It allows short, high-frequency waves to pass through. It is important in radio communications because it reflects low- and medium-frequency radio waves back to the ground.

Sometimes the ionosphere is disturbed by particles from the sun. These disturbances cause natural displays of light in the sky called auroras (see AURORA).

Exosphere The exosphere is the outermost layer of the atmosphere. It begins 300 mi. [480 km] above the earth, but it does not have a definite boundary with outer space. The outer parts of the exosphere contain mostly oxygen and helium gases. The exosphere has a high temperature, ranging up to several thousand degrees centigrade.

This means that the atoms and molecules are moving very fast. But a spacecraft in this layer of very thin air would be in no danger of melting. There are so few atoms and molecules present that they can give very little heat to an object passing through the layer.

Atmospheric pressure and circulation

Look at the top of a desk. Imagine a column of air pressing on it that is about 500 mi. [800 km] high. The total amount of weight on the desk top is called atmospheric pressure. At sea level, the atmosphere has a pressure of 14.7 lb. per sq. in. [1.03 kg per sq. cm].

There are many forces that account for the circulation of the atmosphere. One force is a result of the sun warming the air near the equator more than it warms the air at the poles. The warmer air rises, and it is replaced by air flowing in from colder regions.

In addition, atmospheric pressure varies from one region on Earth to another. Air near the ground tends to flow from areas where the pressure is higher to areas where the pressure is lower. Circulation results as the differences in pressure try to even themselves out. PROJECT 2, 22, 26

ATMOSPHERE (UNIT) An atmosphere is a unit of atmospheric pressure. It equals 14.7 lb. per sq. in. [1.03 kg per sq. cm]. That is the pressure produced by a column of mercury in an upright tube that is 30 in. [76 cm] high. An atmosphere is also equal to 1,013 millibars, and 101,325 newtons per square meter. Air has a pressure of approximately one atmosphere at sea level.
See also BAROMETER; MILLIBAR; NEWTON.

ATOLL (ā′tôl′) An atoll is a ring or horseshoe-shaped group of coral islands surrounding a body of seawater. Atolls are found in tropical seas, where corals grow best (see CORAL). The water must be shallow, with much sunlight upon it. Normally, the lower limit for coral growth is between 197 ft. [60 m] and 295 ft. [90 m]. A very unusual drilling at the Eniwetok Atoll in the Marshall Islands discovered at least 5,000 ft. [1,525 m] of coral.

There are a number of theories why coral can form to such a great depth. One suggestion is that sea levels have slowly risen, allowing coral to form in further layers. Another theory explains the formation of layers of coral as the result of the slow sinking of land beneath the seas.

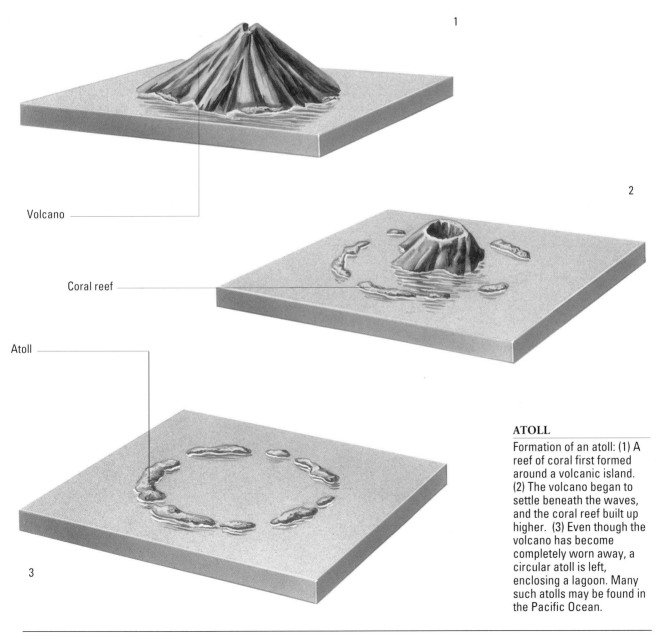

1

Volcano

Coral reef

2

Atoll

3

ATOLL

Formation of an atoll: (1) A reef of coral first formed around a volcanic island. (2) The volcano began to settle beneath the waves, and the coral reef built up higher. (3) Even though the volcano has become completely worn away, a circular atoll is left, enclosing a lagoon. Many such atolls may be found in the Pacific Ocean.

ATOM

An atom is the smallest part of an element having all the properties of that element (see ELEMENT). It is difficult to realize how extremely small an atom is. For example, this page is more than a million atoms thick.

Atoms are made up of even smaller particles. Every atom consists of a central part called a nucleus. Electrons move around the nucleus. The nucleus is very small compared with the size of an atom. If the diameter of an atom were the size of a football field (100 yd. or 91.44 m), the nucleus would be the size of a pea. In this sense, an atom consists mostly of space (see NUCLEUS).

The nucleus is made up of two basic kinds of particles: protons and neutrons. Their masses are almost equal, and they are both about 1,850 times heavier than an electron. This means that almost all the mass of an atom is concentrated in the nucleus. The mass of the nucleus is less than the mass of its protons and neutrons. This is because when the particles form a nucleus, some of their mass is converted to energy to hold them together. The neutrons have no electric charge, but both the protons and the electrons are charged. The proton is positively charged, and the electron has an equal negative charge. An atom has an equal number of protons and electrons. This makes the atom electrically neutral (see ELECTRON; NEUTRON; PROTON.)

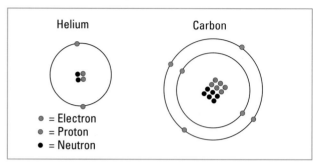

HELIUM AND CARBON ATOMS
A model of a helium atom is shown on the left, and a model of a carbon atom is shown on the right. Both have their inner shell filled with two electrons. The models are not drawn to scale. In reality, the nucleus is only about 1/100 of the total size of the atom.

Electrons, protons, and neutrons are referred to as subatomic particles. Protons and neutrons are, in turn, made up of even smaller particles called quarks (see QUARK). The rest of this article focuses on protons, neutrons, and electrons.

Atoms of each different element are different. The difference between one kind of atom and another lies in the number of protons in the nucleus.

The number of electrons moving around the nucleus is the same as the number of protons inside it. Hydrogen has one proton in the nucleus and one electron outside it. Uranium has a nucleus containing 92 protons and therefore 92

EARLY THEORIES OF ATOMIC STRUCTURE
Some of the ways in which early scientists pictured the atom are shown. (1) John Dalton, in 1802, imagined atoms to be like billiard balls. (2) J.J. Thomson, in 1901, thought the electrons were scattered throughout the atom. (3) Ernest Rutherford, in 1911, pictured electrons orbiting the nucleus. (4) In 1913, Neils Bohr pictured the orbits arranged as layers, or shells.

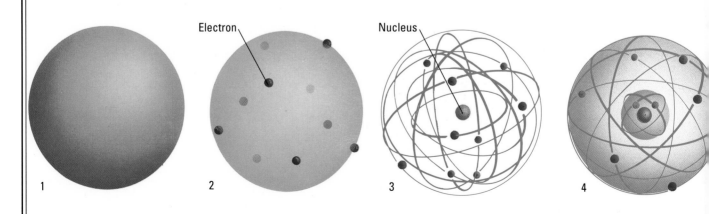

NUCLEUS

The nucleus contains two basic kinds of particles: protons and neutrons. Scientists have discovered that these are made up of even smaller particles called quarks.

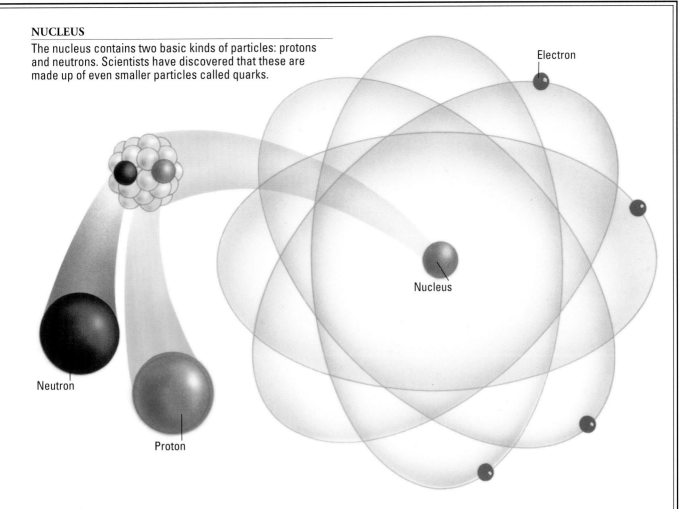

Electron

Nucleus

Neutron

Proton

electrons surrounding it. These electrons are flying around the nucleus at great speeds. Their arrangement is very complicated and it is difficult to know where any electron is at any moment. However, a simple way of thinking about them is to imagine them to be in orbit around the nucleus, like a spacecraft orbiting the earth or a planet orbiting the sun. These orbits are called shells. There are several different shells. The farther away the shell is from the nucleus, the more electrons it can hold. The shell closest to the nucleus can only hold two electrons. This shell may only have one electron, as it does in a hydrogen atom. When this shell has two electrons, as in helium, the shell is said to be filled. The second shell can hold up to eight electrons, the third up to eighteen, and so on. The electrons in an atom always arrange themselves so that the shells nearest the nucleus are filled first.

The outer electrons are responsible for the chemical properties of the atom. Atoms are most

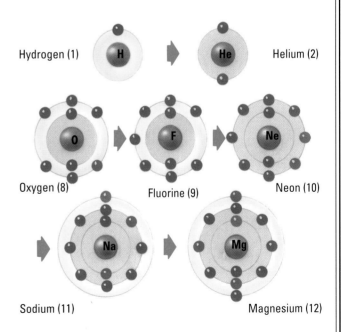

Hydrogen (1)   Helium (2)

Oxygen (8)   Fluorine (9)   Neon (10)

Sodium (11)   Magnesium (12)

ELECTRON SHELLS

The diagram above shows the build-up of electrons in different atoms. Hydrogen, the simplest atom, has only one electron in its first shell. Oxygen, which has eight electrons, has its first shell filled with two electrons and has six in its next shell.

stable when their outer shells are filled. If they have an unfilled outer shell, they try to become more stable by forming collections of atoms called molecules (see MOLECULE). Some atoms, such as helium, do not have any unfilled shells. These atoms, therefore, do not form ordinary molecules. These elements occur in nature as single atoms. They are said to be monatomic. Atoms of some other elements, such as hydrogen, are joined together in pairs by bonds. Such molecules are said to be diatomic.

Sometimes an atom loses an electron. It then becomes positively charged. An atom can also gain an electron and become negatively charged. An atom that gains or loses an electron is said to be ionized. The charged atom is called an ion. Since unlike charges attract each other, positive ions attract negative ions. When they come together, they form a chemical bond. This kind of bond is called an ionic or electrovalent bond. When atoms combine in this way, they both end up with completed outer shells (see BONDING; IONS AND IONIZATION; VALENCE).

Atoms can also bind together by sharing electrons. The bond formed is called a covalent bond. The electrons spend part of the time with one atom and part of the time with the other. In this way, they can make the outer shells of both atoms full.

Helium gas always consists of single atoms.

Hydrogen gas usually consists of pairs of atoms sharing their electrons.

Ozone gas consists of triplets of oxygen atoms sharing their electrons.

ATOMIC GROUPING

The drawings show molecules that contain only one kind of atom. The atoms of helium occur singly. Helium is a monatomic gas.

Isotopes

Just as atoms can have different numbers of electrons and protons, they can also have different numbers of neutrons in the nucleus. Atoms having the same number of protons but a different number of neutrons from other atoms are still atoms of the same element. However, they are said to be isotopes of that element. For example, hydrogen exists in three different isotopes, called normal hydrogen, deuterium, and tritium. Normal hydrogen has one proton and no neutrons in its nucleus. Deuterium has one proton and one neutron in its nucleus. Tritium has one proton and two neutrons (see ISOTOPE).

Isotope	Symbol	Protons	Neutrons	Electrons	Atom
Hydrogen	1 H 1	1	0	1	
Deuterium	2 H 1	1	1	1	
Tritium	3 H 1	1	2	1	

ISOTOPES

Isotopes are atoms of the same element that have different numbers of neutrons in the nucleus. The table shows details of isotopes of hydrogen. To identify each isotope, a symbol is used, with numerals indicating the number of particles in the nucleus as well as the number of electrons.

Investigating the atom

Atoms are too small to be seen in an optical microscope or an electron microscope. They can, however, be seen with a field ion microscope. The atoms appear only as patches of light with little shape. Scientists do not have to see atoms in order to learn about them. Chemists can discover how atoms react together by seeing how large samples of substances react together. Physicists can find out how atoms are arranged in crystal lattices. They do this by passing X rays through the crystals and studying the resulting pattern of X rays (see CRYSTAL). The spectrum of light produced in a spectroscope gives information on the arrangement of electrons inside an atom (see SPECTROSCOPE). Physicists can also research how atoms react when they are

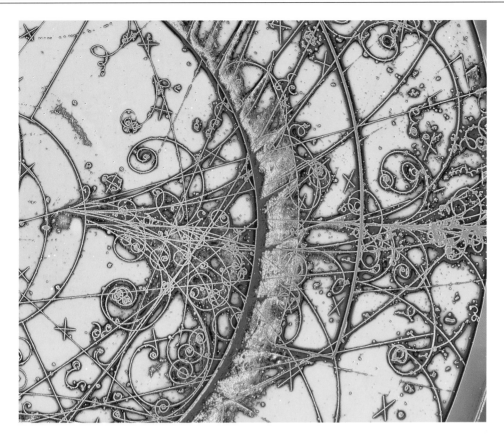

Subatomic particles can be studied using a bubble chamber, which is a tank full of a superheated liquid. As the particles move through the liquid, they create a series of bubbles. The shapes of the bubble trails give scientists information about the particles.

bombarded or collided, using three kinds of chambers: the bubble, cloud, and spark chambers. As the atoms pass through these chambers, they leave behind visible trails. Photographs are taken of the trails, which the physicists later study (see ACCELERATORS, PARTICLE).

The most recent atomic research involves the use of trapping devices to isolate, count, and study atoms. By the mid-1980s, physicists were able to trap a small group of sodium atoms, about 100,000, for one or two seconds. Larger traps now hold small groups of atoms for more than two minutes. Various trapping systems involve the use of magnetism, laser or polarized light, or systems to cool the atoms (see LASER; MAGNETISM; POLARIZED LIGHT). Multiphoton resonance ionization (MPRI) is another trapping device that allows scientists to count very small groups or even single atoms.

These trapping devices are used with cooling devices. Cooling devices are what actually slow the motion of the atoms. An atom would have no motion at all if it were cooled to -459.67°F [-273.15°C], which is absolute zero. Scientists came close to achieving this temperature and stopping the motion of an atom in 1989. Scientists at the Massachusetts Institute of Technology succeeded in holding 500 billion hydrogen atoms in a trap for 20 minutes at an estimated temperature of 0.04°F [0.02°C] above absolute zero. However, scientists still have not been able to actually reach absolute zero. By slowing atoms, scientists hope to build more precise atomic clocks and better satellite navigation systems. They also hope to make new discoveries about atomic collisions (see ABSOLUTE ZERO; CLOCK; NAVIGATION).

Atomic energy Atomic energy is energy produced by the nucleus of an atom. For this reason, it is better called nuclear energy. This energy can be obtained by fission or by fusion. In fission, the nuclei (plural of *nucleus*) of large atoms split to form smaller nuclei. When they split, the nuclei lose some of their mass. The lost mass has been converted to energy. Fusion occurs when the nuclei of small atoms, such as those of hydrogen, join together, with a resultant release of energy (see FISSION; FUSION; NUCLEAR ENERGY; NUCLEAR PHYSICS).

ATOMIC NUMBER An atomic number is the number of protons in the nucleus of an atom. Since each proton in the nucleus has one positive electric charge, the total number of positive electric charges in the nucleus is equal to the atomic number. This number is the same as the number of electrons surrounding the nucleus of a neutral atom. Each of these electrons has one negative charge.

Every element has a different atomic number. This provides a way to identify any element. In the periodic table, the elements are arranged in order according to atomic number.

See also ATOM; ELECTRON; ELEMENT; NUCLEUS; PROTON.

ATOMIC WEIGHT *See* RELATIVE ATOMIC MASS.

ATP ATP, adenosine triphosphate, is an important chemical substance that is usually formed in the mitochondria of living cells (see KREBS CYCLE; MITOCHONDRIA). ATP stores energy for use within the cells. When energy is needed for metabolic activities, such as nerve, gland, or muscle function in animals or the changing of glucose to form proteins, cellulose, or starch in plants, ATP supplies it (see METABOLISM).

ATP contains three phosphate molecules that are held together by energy-rich chemical bonds. When energy is required, one of these bonds breaks, releasing energy. One phosphate splits off, leaving ADP (adenosine diphosphate). This reaction (ATP —> ADP + P + energy) is controlled by enzymes (see ENZYME).

The cells constantly renew their supplies of ATP. Animals form the energy-rich ATP by using energy released from digested food (see RESPIRATION). Plants renew their ATP supplies during photosynthesis by using energy from sunlight (see PHOTOSYNTHESIS). Although ATP is usually formed in the mitochondria, it is released for use by any part of the cell.

AUDUBON, JOHN JAMES (1785–1851) John James Audubon was one of the first

AUDUBON
John James Audubon was one of the most famous naturalists and bird artists of the eighteenth century.

American naturalists and ornithologists to study and paint birds of the United States (see ORNITHOLOGY). His drawings and paintings were of birds in their natural surroundings.

Audubon painted some 1,055 life-sized pictures and had them published in London as *The Birds of America.* Original copies of this book are now very valuable. They are found mostly in large libraries and museums.

Audubon did much to publicize the value of wildlife. The National Audubon Society was named in his honor and is still one of the major wildlife societies in the United States.

AUK Auks are seabirds belonging to the family Alcidae. They have short wings, and their legs are set far back on their bodies. They are excellent swimmers and divers, using their wings as paddles and their feet as rudders. Auks are usually black and white. They spend the winters feeding on fish and plankton in the northern Atlantic and Pacific

AUK
With their short, stubby wings and legs set far back on their bodies, auks are well adapted to swimming and diving.

oceans (see PLANKTON). In the spring, huge colonies of auks come ashore, nesting in the cliffs. The female lays one or two eggs in cracks in the rocks. The parents stay with their young until they are well grown.

One species, the great auk, became extinct in 1844. This bird could not fly. It was hunted ruthlessly for its feathers and meat. The existing twenty-one species of alcids are about one-third the size of the great auk and are able to fly. The little auk, or dovekie, is about 8 in. [20 cm] long and feeds on plankton. Other small auks are called auklets or sea sparrows.

AURORA (ô rôr′ə) An aurora is a natural display of light in the sky. Occasionally, the night sky in the Northern Hemisphere glows with bright green, red, blue, and yellow colors. This is called the aurora borealis. The aurora australis is the name for the same display that occurs in the Southern Hemisphere. The auroras are usually located near the north or south poles at heights of 50 to 100 mi. [80 to 160 km]. Some may be as high as 600 mi. [1,000 km].

When there is an increase in sunspot activity, the clouds of charged atomic particles that the sun sends out increase in strength (see SOLAR WIND; SUNSPOT). These particles travel through space in all directions. As they enter the earth's atmosphere, the magnetism at the poles changes the direction and speed of the particles. These particles then collide with air molecules in the cold, thin ionosphere, the third layer of the atmosphere. This collision causes colored light. This process may continue for hours, often lighting the sky for an entire evening.

See also MAGNETIC STORM.

AUTOMATION Simply stated, automation is the use of machines to run other machines. It is a way of making a device, a process, or a system operate automatically. Human effort is not involved in the actual work. Once a person has planned what the machine should do and has turned on the power, the machine does the rest. Unlike workers whom they replace, such machines do not make mistakes, get tired, or take time off for sickness or vacations. However, they also cannot think for themselves or make judgments. They can only do what people have instructed them to do.

The word *automation* first came into general use around 1950. However, automation really began with the steam-operated textile machines of eighteenth-century England. The steam engines that powered those machines were fitted with automatic valves and devices that controlled their speed. In 1801, Joseph Marie Jacquard, a Frenchman, suggested the use of cards with a pattern of holes punched in them. He used the cards to automate a loom. Similar punched cards and paper tapes were used to control various kinds of

AURORA

The display of colored lights in the sky known as the aurora borealis is produced when tiny charged particles from the sun collide with air molecules high in the atmosphere.

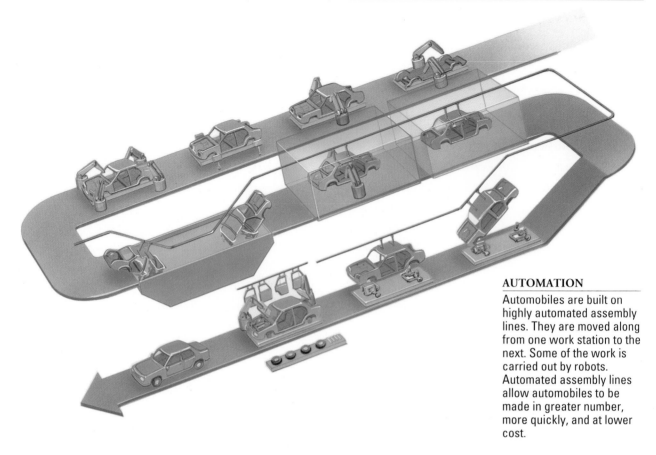

AUTOMATION

Automobiles are built on highly automated assembly lines. They are moved along from one work station to the next. Some of the work is carried out by robots. Automated assembly lines allow automobiles to be made in greater number, more quickly, and at lower cost.

automated machines before faster and more convenient control media, such as floppy disks, were invented. Early in the twentieth century, American industry used automated machines in the mass production of automobiles. Because machines often surpassed human workers in job performance, many other industries turned to automation.

Science and technology soon responded to the call of business and industry for faster and more efficient production. New scientific discoveries, especially in electronics, changed the modern world much as the inventions of the Industrial Revolution had done. Advances in radio, television, telecommunications, and aviation helped lay the groundwork for the dawning of the space age in the 1950s.

Space travel posed a new set of problems. Automation was the answer to many of them. How could human beings control something as fast as a rocket in flight? The need for instant access to information was vital. This need was met by computers, which can do high-speed calculations. The need for speedy, accurate, nonhuman performance was met by totally automated machines called robots. Computers and robots working together seem to have unlimited capacity for getting things done rapidly and efficiently. It is not surprising, then, that a race toward total automation has developed among the United States, Japan, and Germany. Largely responsible for this forward leap of automation is the great progress made in computer science.

Computers are being used to control most automated industrial systems. Petroleum refineries, for example, are being run almost completely by computer. The few workers needed to operate the plant spend most of their time in a control room watching dials and other indicators. Many other large plants are operated in this way—for example, textile mills, steel mills, and automobile and aircraft plants. Advanced computer systems control the equipment of the banking industry and many other large businesses. Also, because computers perform at rates that may be as high as millions of operations per second, their use in scientific and technological laboratories is invaluable. *See also* COMPUTER; ROBOTICS.

AUTOMOBILE

Modern automobiles, or cars, are four-wheeled, self-propelled passenger vehicles. A gasoline, diesel, or electric engine provides the force that moves an automobile. The smallest automobiles carry two people: the driver and the passenger. The largest autos can carry ten or more people. Automobiles are produced in large, automated factories that build many vehicles each day (see AUTOMATION). The largest automobile plants in the United States are near Detroit, Michigan.

History In 1769, Nicolas Cugnot of France used a steam engine to propel a crude wheeled vehicle. The first practical internal combustion engine was built by a French inventor, Etienne Lenoir, about 1860 (see ENGINE). A German engineer, Nikolaus Otto, built a more efficient gasoline engine in 1861. In 1885, Karl Benz and Gottlieb Daimler, of Germany, used Otto's engine on four-wheeled carriages to make the first true automobiles (see BENZ, KARL). Early models were built slowly by hand and were expensive. In 1913, Henry Ford, an American, introduced the conveyor belt to carry automobile parts on assembly lines (see CONVEYOR; FORD, HENRY). This made it possible to produce many automobiles in a short

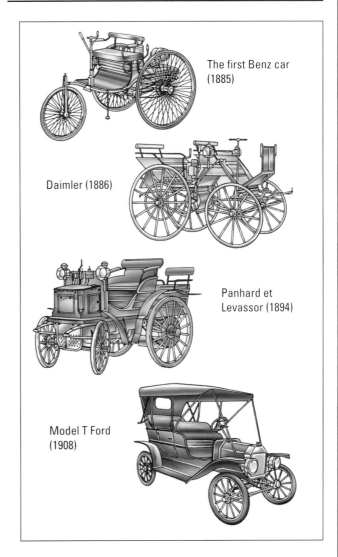

The first Benz car (1885)

Daimler (1886)

Panhard et Levassor (1894)

Model T Ford (1908)

FIRST CARS

Within 20 years cars developed from an open tricycle with an engine at the back to a covered four-wheeled vehicle with the engine at the front (above). The steering mechanism had also changed, from a side-to-side tiller to a steering wheel.

EARLY MANUFACTURING

Early automobile manufacturers, such as the Ford Motor Company, were pioneers in the development of mass production. Workers in an early Ford plant are pictured in the historic photograph at left.

time. Ford was able to lower his prices so that many more people could afford to own automobiles. Other manufacturers did the same.

There were several major United States automobile manufacturers in the 1920s. Of them, only three are still in business: Ford Motor Company, General Motors, and Chrysler.

After World War II (1939–1945), Volkswagen, a German company, began to sell many of its small cars in the United States. They were called Beetles. Today, cars produced in Germany, Japan, and other countries account for a large number of all automobile sales in the United States.

AUTOMOBILE DESIGN

There are many steps involved in the design and manufacture of today's automobiles. Designers often start with drawings of their ideas (top). Full-size models and prototypes are not built until all of the designs have been refined by the design team (above).

Assembly An automobile body is attached to a structure of steel beams called a chassis. The chassis is very strong. It absorbs many strains and stresses. The body consists of thin sheet metal with some structural steel beams built in for added strength. Some bodies are made of aluminum or fiberglass.

Automobiles are built on assembly lines. Groups of workers—or, increasingly, robots—install different parts as the uncompleted automobiles are moved past them. Major units, such as engines and transmissions, are assembled on their own assembly lines. When completed, they are brought to the main assembly line and put into the automobile at the proper time. Computers are used to keep track of all the hundreds of parts that go into each car. Completed automobiles are rolled off the end of the assembly line, tested, and delivered to dealers by trains and large trucks.

Engines The gasoline engine is used as the power source in most automobiles. Some autos are powered by diesel engines (see DIESEL). Diesel engines are heavier and more expensive than gasoline engines. They last longer than gasoline engines, however. Electric engines that run on stored electricity in batteries have been developed for small cars to be used for city driving. They are not in wide use. Some manufacturers have experimented with gas turbine engines for automobiles. However, they are too expensive to produce in quantity (see TURBINE).

Most automobile engines have four, six, or eight cylinders. Gasoline is mixed with air and compressed (squeezed) inside each cylinder. It is ignited with a spark from a spark plug. The explosion forces a piston to move downwards. An arm attached to the piston turns a large shaft at the bottom of the engine called the crankshaft.

Most engines are mounted in the front end of the automobile. Front-mounted engines drive the front wheels rather than the rear wheels in most new automobiles. Some engines are mounted in the rear of the car and drive the rear wheels.

An automobile engine needs electricity to ignite the gas-air mixture in its cylinders. It generates its

MODERN MANUFACTURING
Finally the original idea goes into production. Nowadays, many of these steps are carried out, or assisted, by computers.

TRANSMISSION
The clutch and the gearbox are key parts of the transmission. The gearbox uses large gearwheels to turn smaller gearwheels even faster. This allows the car to go faster. The clutch allows different gears to be meshed together smoothly.

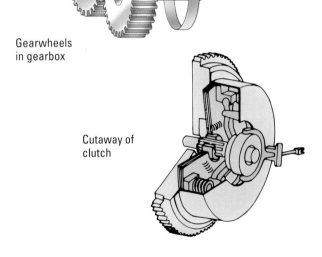

Gearwheels in gearbox

Cutaway of clutch

own electricity with one of two kinds of machines: a generator or an alternator. Some of the electricity is stored in a lead-acid battery. Every car has a battery. Electricity from the battery is used to start the engine and to operate lights and accessories (see BATTERY; GENERATOR, ELECTRICAL).

Engines create a great amount of heat when they are running. The explosions in the cylinders have a temperature of 3,500°F [1,927°C]. Cylinder temperatures must be brought down to about 160°F [71°C] in order to prevent damage to the engine. Cool air is blown across the engine by a fan attached to the front end. In some engines, a cooling system circulates a mixture of water and chemicals around the cylinder walls to cool them. The water-chemical mixture gets hot in the process. It is cooled again by running it through the radiator mounted in front of the engine. Other engines are air cooled.

Lubrication systems circulate oil throughout the engine to reduce friction between moving parts. Exhaust systems remove waste gases that result from combustion in the cylinders. Mufflers reduce the noise caused by this combustion.

Transmission Engine power is transmitted (sent) to the wheels through the transmission, drive shaft, and differential. Together, these parts

are called the drive train. A part called a clutch links the power in the crankshaft with the drive train. The clutch can be mechanical or hydraulic. Mechanical clutches are operated by a foot pedal. Hydraulic clutches operate automatically by fluid pressure (see CLUTCH). The transmission contains gears of different sizes (see GEAR). Manual transmissions require the driver to change gears by moving the gearshift lever. Automatic transmissions do away with clutch pedals and gearshift levers. Gears are shifted automatically by means of hydraulic pressure (see HYDRAULICS). Cars start forward slowly in low gear. Second gear picks up speed. High gear maintains driving, or cruising, speed. Some cars have four or five forward gears.

The drive shaft carries the power from the transmission to the differential. The differential is a set of gears that drives the wheels. When an automobiles goes around a corner, the outside wheel must turn faster because it has a greater distance to travel than the inside wheel. The differential is designed to allow the wheels to turn at different speeds.

Steering, braking, suspension The driver uses the steering wheel to guide the car. The steering wheel turns the steering column. The steering column is linked to the front wheels by a steering box that contains a set of gears. The gears make it easier for the driver to turn the heavy front wheels.

Some cars are equipped with power steering. This allows hydraulic pressure to aid the driver.

Automobiles are required by law to have dual braking systems for safety. The main braking system, operated by a foot pedal, acts on all four wheels. It is a hydraulic system. When the driver steps on the brake, fluid is pumped from a master cylinder to each wheel. The pressure of the fluid works either a drum or a disk that is attached to each wheel (see BRAKE). A second braking system, called the parking brake, is operated by a hand lever. The lever is connected to wires that operate the drum or disk brakes on the rear wheels only. The parking brake will hold a parked car on a hill. It does not have the strength to stop a fast-moving car. Automatic transmissions can be set in positions that lock the gears and prevent the wheels from turning. This will keep a car from moving if it is parked on a hill.

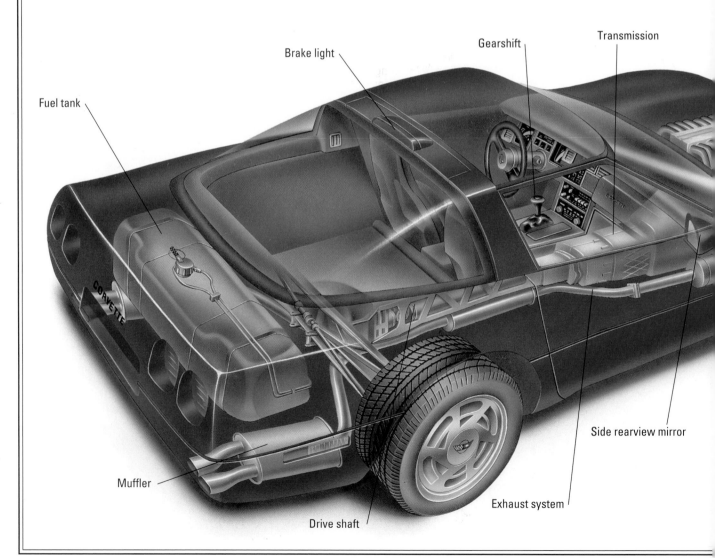

The suspension system on most cars consists of heavy springs and shock absorbers. It helps make the ride more comfortable by cushioning the car when it goes over bumps.

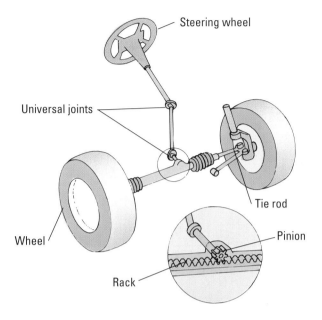

STEERING SYSTEM
The steering system above is known as rack and pinion. When the steering wheel is turned, the pinion (a small gearwheel) moves the rack from side to side. This causes the wheels to turn.

SPORTS CARS
The Chevrolet Corvette is an example of a sports car. It is built with a low, sleek body, and it has broad tires to transmit its engine power to the road. Its 6-liter engine allows it to be driven at speeds of up to 186 miles per hour [299 kph].

Automobile safety Traffic accidents in the United States during recent years have resulted in an average of 50,000 deaths and millions of injuries each year. Many accidents are caused by drivers who drive too fast. A national speed limit of 55 m.p.h. [89 kph] was adopted in the United States in 1974. During the years when it was in effect, the 55 m.p.h. speed limit was credited with saving thousands of lives. In the mid-1980s, the U.S. Congress allowed states to increase the speed limit to 65 m.p.h. [105 kph] on certain roads. The result has been an increase in traffic-related deaths, according to state traffic records.

Other regulations have recently been enacted to try to save lives. For example, most states require small children to be placed in special protective seats while riding in the car. Also, the United States requires certain safety devices to be installed on all new cars and trucks sold in the United States. These safety devices include lap belts, shoulder harnesses, shatterproof windows, collapsible steering columns, and impact-resistant bumpers. In the past, many drivers were reluctant to use their lap belts and shoulder harnesses. The result was thousands of injuries and deaths. Most states have passed laws requiring drivers and passengers to use their lap belts and shoulder harnesses. In 1987, the government began requiring that automobile manufacturers start building cars with "passive" restraints such as automatic seat belts.

Automobile manufacturers have been equipping cars with driver-side automatic air bags since 1994. By 1998, all passenger cars will be equipped with driver- and passenger-side air bags. Light trucks will follow in 1999. An air bag is an inflatable, pillowlike cushion that is stored in the steering wheel. Some cars also have an air bag for the front-seat passenger that is stored in the dashboard. Devices in the car detect the rapid deceleration, or slowing down, that occurs during a crash, and the air bag inflates. The air bag cushions the driver's or passenger's body as it is thrust forward. The air bag later deflates. The high degree of protection that air bags can provide has caused many consumer activist groups to work in favor of laws requiring air bags as standard

equipment on all automobiles and trucks sold in the United States.

Tires can be another safety feature. Today's tires adhere to road surfaces better and are manufactured to help give better gas mileage. They also last longer. In fact, automobiles in general have become not only safer but more efficient over the years. Improved suspensions and braking systems enable automobiles to handle better than ever. Automobile manufacturers have added steel supports to vital areas of the automobile body. The supports help the body withstand impacts with greater safety for the passengers. Smaller engines that use less fuel have replaced larger ones without sacrificing too much power. The National Highway Traffic Safety Administration (NHTSA) sets the safety standards for new automobiles. It sometimes orders manufacturers to recall cars that have been found to have safety defects. A car that has been recalled must be repaired by the manufacturer at no charge to the owner.

Automobiles and the environment The widespread use of automobiles has led to serious environmental concerns. The exhaust from automobile engines produces about 20 percent of the carbon dioxide released into the atmosphere every year in the United States. Carbon dioxide is the main gas responsible for the greenhouse effect. In the greenhouse effect, pollution in the atmosphere helps trap the sun's heat. This causes the earth's temperature to rise (see GREENHOUSE EFFECT).

Automobiles also give off carbon monoxide, nitrogen dioxide, and sulfur dioxide. These pollutants contribute to acid rain and smog (see ACID RAIN; AIR; SMOG). The running of automobile air conditioners releases chlorofluorocarbons, known as CFCs, into the air (see CHLOROFLUOROCARBON). CFCs destroy the protective ozone layer of the upper stratosphere (see ATMOSPHERE; OZONE). In 1990, the Clean Air Act was passed. It called for the phasing out of CFCs by the end of the 1990s, but the Bush administration pushed the date to 1995. New cars will now be designed with a CFC substitute, HFC-134a (R-134).

In spite of these concerns, the use of automobiles is still increasing. Scientists are researching other ways to reduce the amount of pollution from automobiles. One of these solutions was the widespread use of unleaded fuel that began in the mid-1970s to reduce lead emissions. Harmful emissions from unleaded fuel can be reduced further by using catalytic converters (see CATALYTIC CONVERTER). They convert harmful gases, including carbon monoxide and nitrogen oxides, into safer gases, such as carbon dioxide, nitrogen, and oxygen. Catalytic converters are required by law in most states as part of the states' emission-control standards. Emission-control standards set the maximum amount of pollution that can be released in automobile exhaust. Cars must be tested periodically to determine the amount of harmful emissions being released in their exhaust. Other ways of reducing pollution involve public transportation, ride sharing, and the development of electric cars and engines that require less fuel.

Aviation is the science of designing, developing, building, and flying aircraft. As long ago as the 1500s, the Italian Leonardo da Vinci designed wings that would flap for a person to use in flight. However, as far as we know, Leonardo never built a full-size model for flying. He also designed helicopters and parachutes. The first human beings on record to fly were Pilâtre de Rozier and the Marquis d'Arlandes. They made their flight in a hot-air balloon made by the Montgolfier brothers of France. The balloon crisscrossed Paris at a height of up to 1,500 ft. [450 m] for 25 minutes.

In the early 1800s, Sir George Cayley, an English scientist, developed and flew the first glider. He was the first person to recognize that fixed, curved wings are better than flapping wings for heavier-than-air craft. Cayley became known as "The Father of Aviation." At about the same time, a Frenchman, Henri Giffard, built a cigar-shaped balloon capable of carrying a person. It was filled with hydrogen gas and powered by a steam engine that turned a propeller. It was the first airship. In the 1800s, Otto Lilienthal, of Germany, and Octave Chanute and Samuel Langley, of the United States, improved upon gliders.

In 1903, two American brothers, Wilbur and Orville Wright, built an aircraft powered by a home-built gasoline engine that drove a propeller. On December 17, 1903, Orville Wright made the first successful powered flight at Kitty Hawk, North Carolina. The airplane was named *Flyer*. It stayed in the air for 12 seconds (see WRIGHT BROTHERS).

In 1909, a Frenchman, Louis Bleriot, flew a plane of his own design from France to England, across the English Channel. Lighter-than-air craft were still being developed at that time. Count Ferdinand von Zeppelin, of Germany, built a huge, metal-framed airship called a dirigible. It was filled with hydrogen. Dirigibles carried

THE FIRST FLIGHT

The first flight in aviation history was made in a hot-air balloon in 1783 by the Montgolfier brothers. An artist's sketch of their balloon is shown.

BIPLANES

Orville Wright made the first successful powered flight in aviation history at Kitty Hawk, North Carolina, in 1903 in the biplane (double-winged plane) above. An illustration of the parts of this airplane is shown below.

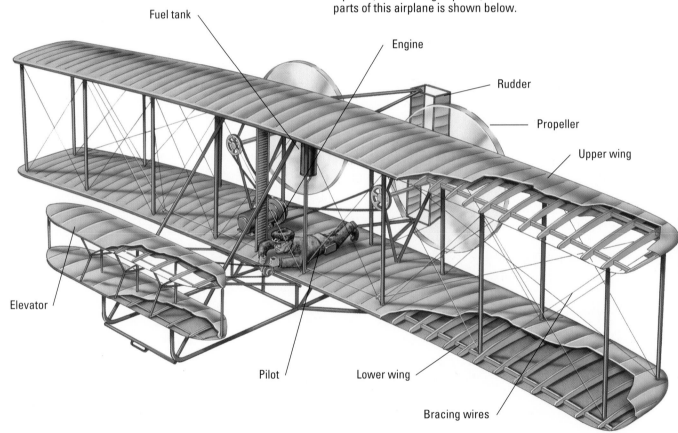

Fuel tank

Engine

Rudder

Propeller

Upper wing

Elevator

Pilot

Lower wing

Bracing wires

passengers and were powered by several engines. The name *Zeppelin* became synonymous with dirigible (see DIRIGIBLE).

World War I (1914–1918) brought about many new developments in aviation. Dirigibles were used for observation and for bombing missions. Planes of all shapes and sizes were built for military use even though they were not thought of as

major weapons at that time. Most designs featured two wings, one placed over the other. They were called biplanes. Triplanes had three wings. With the introduction of metal construction, single-wing planes, or monoplanes, started to come into use toward the end of World War I. Fighter planes and scout planes had one engine. Machine guns were mounted on most planes. They were timed to fire through the spinning propeller without hitting it. Aerial fights between planes became known as "dogfights." Larger planes, called bombers, had two or more engines.

In 1916, the first commercial airline was started. Air Transport and Travel Ltd., carried passengers throughout England in modified DeHavilland bombers.

In the 1920s, airmail routes were started in the United States. "Barnstorming" pilots toured the country in their planes, introducing aviation to small towns and cities. They put on flying shows and took people for plane rides. In 1923, Juan de la Cierva, of Spain, designed and flew the first autogyro. It was the forerunner to the helicopter (see HELICOPTER). In 1926, Commander Richard Byrd, of the United States, flew an airplane over the North Pole. In 1927, Charles Lindbergh became one of America's heroes when he flew his plane, the *Spirit of St. Louis*, nonstop from Long Island, New York to Paris in 33½ hours. In 1929, the *Graf Zeppelin*, a German dirigible, flew 21,870 mi. [35,200 km] around the world in just three weeks. The *Graf Zeppelin* was 775 ft. [236.3 m] long.

The air transport industry began to grow in the early 1930s. In the United States, the Ford Trimotor, a passenger plane with three engines, was used by most airlines. Many cities built airports (see AIRPORT). Airline routes were extended to more and more locations. The Boeing Aircraft Company built the first all-metal passenger plane, the Model 247, in 1933. It was a monoplane and had landing gear that could be folded up into the body of the plane during flight. It also had deicing equipment that allowed it to fly at high altitudes and in bad weather. The deicers kept ice from forming on the wings. The Boeing DC-3 transport plane was developed from this model. Thousands of DC-3s were built by Boeing between 1935 and 1945. They were durable and dependable and became a familiar sight in the sky. DC-3s were the most used transport planes in the 1940s, especially during World War II (1939–1945), when they were referred to as C-47s. Some DC-3s built in the late 1940s are still flying.

In May 1937, the German dirigible *Hindenburg*, which used hydrogen gas, exploded during a landing at Lakehurst, New Jersey, after a flight across the Atlantic. Many passengers were killed. Commercial dirigible flights were stopped soon after and never resumed. Hot-air balloons owned by individuals and small airships used for advertising or to carry television cameras are the only lighter-than-air craft in use today. Modern airships are filled with helium, a gas that does not burn.

World War II brought many new developments in aviation. The airplane became a major weapon of war for the first time. Bombers dropped bombs on enemy targets. They were protected by small, fast, and heavily armed fighter planes. "Air power," as it was called, played a large part in the Allies' victory over Germany and Japan.

During the war, aircraft manufacturers expanded their plants in order to meet military needs. Assembly lines were set up so that large numbers

AIR TRAVEL THROUGH HISTORY

The first fighter planes, built during World War I, were biplanes (below left). Luxury air travel in the 1920s and 1930s was provided by dirigibles (below right).

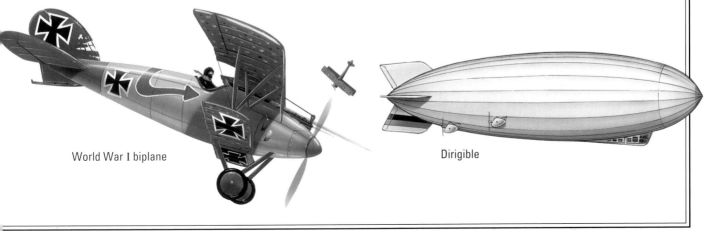

World War I biplane

Dirigible

Modern strike aircraft

AIR TRAVEL THROUGH HISTORY
Today, most aircraft, from small business planes to airliners, are all-metal, jet-propelled monoplanes. The supersonic airliner has greatly reduced flying time between Europe and the United States.

Business jet

of planes could be built quickly. In the United States, fifty thousand planes a year were built. New materials were used that improved the quality of airplanes. Larger and more powerful engines let planes fly faster and higher. Fighter planes flew at 300 to 400 m.p.h. [480 to 640 kph]. Jet engines were developed toward the end of the war but did not come into wide use until after 1945.

Aviation today The air transport industry has continued to grow. There are now thousands of airports in the United States. Many jet airliners fly at about 600 m.p.h. [960 kph], and jets carry a total of more than one billion passengers each year. Special electronic equipment allows planes to be flown safely in almost any kind of weather.

Today, so-called jumbo jets can carry up to five hundred passengers. Such planes also carry cargo. The *Concorde*, a passenger airliner developed by the British and the French, can fly about 1,350 m.p.h. [2,200 kph]. It has cut flying time between Europe and the United States to about three hours.

Many business firms whose executives travel a great deal found that they could save money by owning their own planes. Although these planes are usually smaller than commercial jets, many of them fly as fast as commercial airliners and have navigation instruments similar to those of the larger planes.

Throughout the history of aviation, interest in recreational flying has always been high. Many people own their own planes just for the thrill of being able to fly. Usually these privately owned

Modern jet airliner

planes are small, propeller-driven craft that can carry two to four people. A new kind of recreational airplane also has become popular. These are the microlights and ultralights, gliderlike planes with a small engine, wings, and a seat or harness to hold the pilot.

Perhaps the most important advance in aviation since the jet engine was the successful testing of the space shuttle *Columbia*. The space shuttle is the first reusable spacecraft. It is launched like a rocket but lands like an airplane. It made its first flight in April 1981. The first four were made to find out how well the space shuttle would work. On later flights, communications satellites were repaired in space, and new ones were launched. Eventually, the space shuttle may have many uses, including carrying people from one space station to another.

In the mid-1970s, when the cost of oil rose sharply, commercial and cargo transport airlines were seriously affected. Higher fuel costs meant that unless the large airplanes flew at full capacity all the time, they would not be profitable. Most of the major airlines and manufacturers seemed to agree on the need for a fuel-efficient transport that would carry 150 to 200 passengers. The first of these, the Boeing 757 and 767, began operating in 1982.

The United States government regulates aviation through the Federal Aviation Administration (FAA). The FAA is responsible for overseeing safety and progress in aviation.

See also AERODYNAMICS; AERONAUTICS; AIRPLANE; SPACE EXPLORATION.

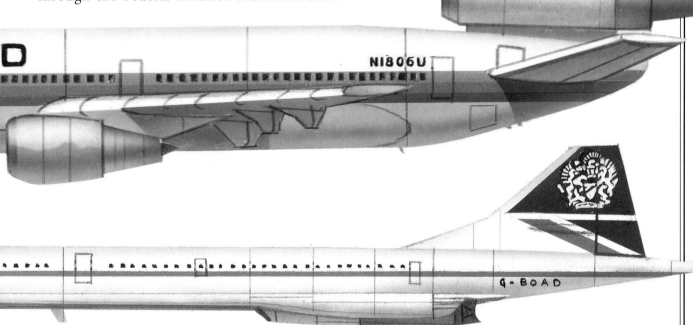

Supersonic airliner

GLIDERS
Modern gliders (right) can soar thousands of feet above the earth for hours.

AVOCADO (ăv′ə kä′dō) An avocado is a fruit grown from a tree of the same name. The tree belongs to the family Lauraceae. It was originally found in tropical South America. The avocado is now planted in warm regions around the world. The fruit is pear-shaped with a green, thick skin. The flesh is yellow green and coarse. It is often eaten in sandwiches or salads or used to make a food called guacamole. The fruit is also called an alligator pear.

AVOCADO
The avocado, or alligator pear, has a rough, green skin and pale green flesh. It is used to make a Mexican dish called guacamole.

AVOCET (ăv′ə sĕt′) An avocet is a wading bird that belongs to the family Recurvirostridae. There are four species of avocets. One is found in North America. The others are found in South America, Australia, and Eurasia. The avocet lives along the shoreline. It feeds by swinging its curved beak, held partly open, through shallow water. It eats small insects and crustaceans.

AVOCET
Avocets are long-legged wading birds. The upward-curving bill of this bird is a special adaptation for feeding under the water.

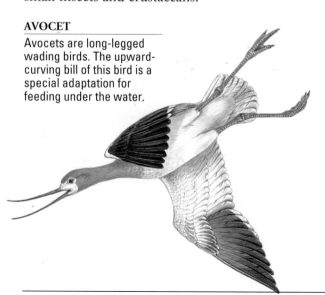

AVOGADRO, AMEDEO (1776–1856) Amedeo Avogadro was an Italian physicist who made several important discoveries about molecules. In 1811, he stated that equal volumes of any gases at the same temperature and pressure contain the same number of molecules. This statement, known as Avogadro's law, is a principle used in a method of finding relative atomic masses.

A mole is the molecular weight of a substance stated in grams. One mole of any substance contains 6.023×10^{23} molecules. This number is called Avogadro's constant or Avogadro's number. Avogadro was the first person to tell the difference between an atom and a molecule. This was necessary to obtain correct values for relative atomic masses and relative molecular masses. It was not until after Avogadro's death that his work was accepted.

See also MOLE (UNIT); RELATIVE ATOMIC MASS; RELATIVE MOLECULAR MASS.

AXIL The axil is the angle between the lower leaf or leaf stem and the branch from which it is growing. The axil is located just above the node. Branches, flowers, leaves, or thorns grow from buds, which form at the nodes. In some plants, such as the lily, a bud may form in the axil that can be used to grow a new plant.

See also PLANT KINGDOM.

AXIL
The axil is the angle between a leaf or leaf stem and the stem or branch from which it grows.

Axil

AZIMUTH (ăz′ə məth) Azimuth is the position or bearing of an object on Earth or in the sky in relation to a fixed point, usually north. It is measured as an angle clockwise from 0° to 360°. So east is 90°, south is 180°, and west is 270°.

In sea navigation, measuring the azimuths of stars lets sailors know where they are in the ocean. Surveyors and mapmakers also use azimuths.

See also NAVIGATION.

B

BABBAGE, CHARLES (1792–1871)

Charles Babbage was an English mathematician whose work helped lead to the development of the modern computer. Babbage began developing his first computing machine, the difference engine, in the early 1820s. However, the necessary precision machine tools and knowledge about electric circuits were unavailable, so Babbage's efforts were unsuccessful. His vision of a computing machine of vast power was a bold step, however. Babbage also invented the speedometer.

BABOON

A baboon is a large monkey found in the rocky regions, open woodlands, and plains of Africa and the Arabian Peninsula. The baboon has a large head and long, sharp teeth. A baboon's arms are about the same length as its legs. A male baboon is about twice the size of a female baboon.

Baboons can carry food in pouches that are inside their cheeks. They feed mostly on plant matter, such as vegetables, fruit, grass, leaves, and roots, but they will also eat some animals, including insects, small mammals, birds, and birds' eggs. Baboons are social animals, living in groups of from ten to two hundred. A large male usually rules. Male baboons, regarded as tough fighters, have been known to attack leopards.

The male hamadryas baboon of the Arabian Peninsula, Ethiopia, Egypt, Sudan, and Somalia has long, gray hair on its head and shoulders. The chacma baboon of South Africa has grayish brown hair on its body and a long collar of hair, called a ruff, around its neck.

BACKSWIMMER

Backswimmers are also called boat bugs. They are one of many types of water bugs. Although backswimmers spend most of their lives in the water, they are able to fly long distances. These insects are small, usually 0.118 to 0.669 in. [3 to 17 mm] in length. They use their long, flat hind legs to paddle through the water. They usually swim on their backs. Their short front legs are used for holding prey. Backswimmers hold a bubble of air between their wings and body. They use the air in the bubble for breathing when they are underwater. This lets them stay underwater for as long as six hours.

BABOON

(1) Hamadryas baboon
(2) Guinea baboon
(3) Olive baboon
(4) Chacma baboon

BACKSWIMMER
Backswimmers use their
long rear legs as oars.

Backswimmers spend the winter buried in the mud at the bottom of a pond or stream.

Backswimmers have sharp beaks, which they use for stabbing fish and other small water animals. They suck the juices out of their victims. Backswimmers can also give painful bites to people.

BACON, FRANCIS (1561–1626) Francis

Bacon was an English philosopher and statesman who developed a scientific method for solving problems. Bacon felt that people should have control over the world around them. The way to get this control, he believed, is through knowledge, and the way to get knowledge is through science.

Bacon stated that there are several things that keep people from getting knowledge. First, people tend to decide something is generally true if they have found it to be true in only one or two cases. They do not test it to find out if it is true in all cases. Second, people base decisions on their own backgrounds and educations. They do not consider that someone with a different background and education might make a different decision. Third, people have to use words to describe something. Because words can be confusing, it is important to be exact in a description. Bacon called these blocks of knowledge *prejudices*.

Once these prejudices are put aside, Bacon said, people can obtain knowledge through inductive reasoning. Inductive reasoning involves making many observations and tests before arriving at any conclusions. Bacon suggested that lists be prepared. One list is for things that are true. A second list is for things that are not true. A third list is for things that are more true than not. For example, suppose a person has seen only red apples. He or she says, "All apples are red." The person believes this until he or she sees a yellow apple. The person may then say, "Most apples are red." If the person had made lists as suggested by Bacon, he or she would find that there are many red apples and many yellow apples. It would be better to say, "There are red apples and yellow apples." Bacon's theory states that the more often an idea is tested and found to be true, the more likely it is to be true.

Because Bacon was highly respected as a philosopher, his views were widely accepted. His work helped greatly in the progress of Renaissance science.

See also INDUCTION (LOGICAL).

SIR FRANCIS BACON
Bacon helped to shape the scientific revolution.

BACTERIA Bacteria (singular, *bacterium*) are

one-celled organisms. They are among the smallest and most widespread of all living things. They may live alone or in groups called colonies. Bacteria belong to the kingdom Monera. Bacteria, or something like them, were probably the first living organisms on earth (see EVOLUTION). They reproduce so quickly that one bacterium can produce millions of others in only a few hours.

Structure and life of bacteria Most bacterial cells have a strong cell wall. Many bacteria have a capsule, a coating surrounding the cell wall. Some

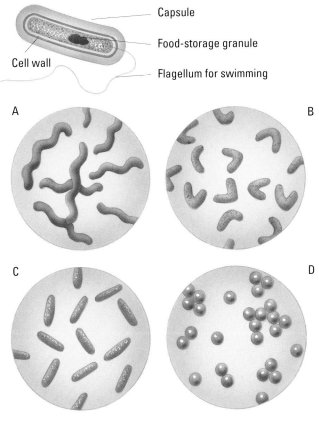

Capsule

Food-storage granule

Cell wall

Flagellum for swimming

A

B

C

D

BACTERIA

Bacteria are microscopic organisms that can be found in every known habitat. They have one of four shapes and can sometimes cause diseases in humans: A—spiral-shaped spirilla, e.g., syphilis; B—curved vibrios, e.g., cholera; C—rod-shaped bacilli, e.g., food poisoning; D—spherical cocci, e.g., sore throats.

bacteria move only by floating passively in the air or water. Most others, though, can move under their own power. Some wriggle from one place to another, while others use a whiplike flagellum to swim (see FLAGELLUM).

Bacteria have one of four shapes. Since they are so small, their shapes can only be seen with a microscope. The coccus (plural, *cocci*) is round. The bacillus (plural, *bacilli*) is rod-shaped. The vibrio (plural, *vibrios*) is shaped like a boomerang. The spirillum (plural, *spirilla*) is spiral-shaped.

Bacteria usually reproduce by fission (see ASEXUAL REPRODUCTION). In fission, the organism splits into two new organisms. It is by rapid fission that bacteria are able to reproduce in such great numbers. At times, bacteria may exchange DNA and other genetic material in a type of sexual reproduction (see DNA). Some bacteria produce endospores for reproduction.

These endospores are very strong. They are often able to survive for extended periods of time in unfavorable conditions.

Bacteria may live in soil, in water, in air, or in other organisms. Although most bacteria live in temperatures between 50 and 104°F [10 to 40°C], some require either very hot or very cold temperatures in order to grow and reproduce. Some bacteria are aerobic and require air to live (see AEROBE). Other bacteria are anaerobic and do not require air to live (see ANAEROBE). Often, anaerobic bacteria die if they are exposed to air.

Some bacteria produce their own food by photosynthesis (see PHOTOSYNTHESIS). Others use simple chemicals as food. Some bacteria are parasites and rely on other living organisms called hosts for food. Some of these parasites harm their hosts, while others live in a state of mutualism (see SYMBIOSIS). Some bacteria are saprophytes and get their food from dead organisms (see SAPROPHYTE). These saprophytic bacteria are important parts of the food chain and of other cycles involving carbon, nitrogen, oxygen, and sulfur (see FOOD CHAIN). Underground oil and natural gas deposits may be the result of the work done by saprophytic bacteria millions of years ago.

Helpful bacteria Some bacteria are useful to humans. Certain bacteria are needed to make cheese, yogurt, and butter. Other bacteria are used in the treatment of sewage and garbage. These bacteria release methane gas as they digest the wastes. In fact, there are cities in the United States and in Europe that use these bacteria as the source of their entire energy supply. One newly discovered type of bacteria can be used to clean up oil spills in the oceans by breaking down the oil into harmless simpler substances. Still other helpful bacteria live in the human body. Some help prevent infections, while others aid in digestion.

Harmful bacteria Some bacteria are harmful to humans. Some can cause food spoilage. This may result in botulism or other forms of food poisoning (see BOTULISM; FOOD POISONING). Some bacteria are pathogenic, or disease causing. Some cause diseases in plants and can destroy entire fields of crops. Some bacteria cause sicknesses in animals, including human beings. Some of the human diseases caused by bacteria are tuberculosis, tetanus, leprosy, syphilis, and gonorrhea. Some bacterial diseases can be fought successfully by the body's own defenses. Vaccinations can help the body build up antibodies to prevent a sickness or to make it less severe (see IMMUNITY). Certain drugs attack only bacteria (see ANTIBIOTIC). The use of antibiotics and sulfa drugs has done much to help control the spread and danger of bacterial diseases and epidemics.

See also DISEASE; INFECTION; KOCH, ROBERT; PASTEUR, LOUIS.

BACTERIOPHAGE (băk tîr′ē ə fāj′) A bacteriophage is any virus that attacks bacteria. The word *bacteriophage* means "bacteria eater." A bacteriophage, like all viruses, is acellular—that is, not a cell. It is made up of a nucleic acid and a protein covering (see BACTERIA; VIRUS).

Bacteriophages are of many different shapes and sizes. Some bacteriophages have hollow, rod-shaped "tails" and sphere- or T-shaped "heads." Others are threadlike. The heads contain nucleic acids (see NUCLEIC ACID). The infection of the bacterial cell by a tailed virus involves attachment of the bacteriophage tail to the cell wall of the bacterium. Then the nucleic acid is injected through the tail into the bacterium. The genetic information in this nucleic acid causes other bacteriophages to be formed inside the bacterium. If the bacterium dies, the new bacteriophages are released and attack other bacteria. Bacteriophages that do not kill the host bacterium may help it to become resistant to certain drugs. Scientists often use bacteriophages to help them understand heredity.

BADGER The badger is a mammal that is a member of the family Mustelidae (see MAMMAL). The family also includes the weasel, skunk, and otter. One species of badger is found in North America, while another species lives in Europe and northern Asia.

BADGER

Badgers, such as this one, are burrowing animals. They usually come out of the holes in which they live only at night.

ACTIVITY *Badger watching*

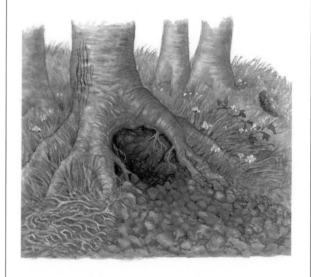

You can look for several signs that a badger's underground home, or set, is nearby. There are often massive heaps of soil a little distance from the entrance to the set, resulting from tunnel digging. You may find small bones of voles, shrews, or mice in these soil heaps. You may also find scraps of bedding material, including hay, dry leaves, and moss. Badgers leave sausage-shaped droppings in shallow, round holes next to well-trodden runs near the set.

Badgers live in holes that they dig in the ground. A badger is a heavyset animal with short legs, short ears, and a doglike head. It grows to a length of 3 ft. [90 cm]. The fur of the badger is silvery gray with black-and-white markings on the head. Badgers are omnivorous, eating many different plants and animals (see OMNIVORE). Much of the badger's food is small mammals, such as mice, which it hunts at night. The badger is not very fast but fights fiercely when attacked. The fur of the badger was once used to make paintbrushes, shaving brushes, and coat trimmings. However, synthetic (human-made) materials have largely replaced badger fur for these purposes.

BAEKELAND, LEO (1863–1944) Leo Baekeland was an American chemist known for the invention of Bakelite, an early plastic. Baekeland was born in Ghent, Belgium. He moved to the United States in 1889.

In 1891, Baekeland invented a sensitive photographic paper. Eastman Kodak bought it from him for one million dollars. Baekeland then tried to invent a synthetic substitute for shellac. He experimented with resins made from phenol and formaldehyde (see RESIN; SHELLAC). In 1909, he produced a resin that was resistant to water and solvents, was an electric insulator, and was easy to shape and cut. Bakelite, named after him, was the first synthetic resin as well as the first thermosetting plastic.
See also BAKELITE.

BAKELITE Bakelite, called phenolic resin by chemists, is a plastic made from phenol and formaldehyde. It was the first truly synthetic plastic. Bakelite was put into commercial use by 1916. It is a thermosetting plastic, one that sets when heated and cannot be molded. Bakelite is dark in color. It is widely used because it resists heat and is comparatively cheap to produce.

Bakelite was once used for the handles of kettles, pans, and irons. It is also a good electric insulator. It is used in the electrical industry and in the home for light switches, plugs, and other electrical fittings. Another use of Bakelite is in laminations with wood, fabric, and other materials to make tough, heatproof substances. The invention of Bakelite opened the door to modern plastics.
See also BAEKELAND, LEO; PLASTIC.

BALANCE A balance is an accurate device used to measure the weight of chemicals and other substances in a laboratory. It consists of a horizontal bar balanced on a thin edge of metal. A pointer attached to the bar moves when the bar is tilted in either direction. Small pans are suspended from each end of the bar. The substance to be weighed is placed in one pan. Numbered weights of different sizes are placed in the other pan. When the weight in both pans is equal, the bar is horizontal, and the pointer is motionless. The weight of the substance can be found by adding up the weights needed to balance the pans.

Laboratory balances are very delicate instruments. They are kept in glass cases to protect them against moisture and gases in the air. Balances must be adjusted for temperature and moisture before each use. Electric balances and microbalances are used for even more accurate measurements.
See also WEIGHT.

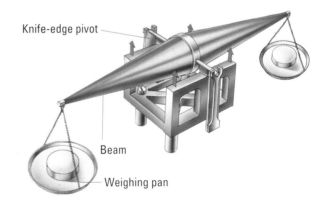

Knife-edge pivot

Beam

Weighing pan

BALANCE

When the beam is balanced on this ancient set of scales, the unknown weight in one pan equals the known weight in the other pan.

BALD EAGLE The bald eagle, also called the white-headed eagle, is a large, North American bird of prey. It is the national bird of the United States. The adult bald eagle reaches a length of 30 to 35 in. [75 to 90 cm], a wingspread of 6.6 ft. [2 m], and a weight of 7.7 to 14.3 lb. [3.5 to 6.5 kg].

The bald eagle is the national emblem of the United States. It is in danger of extinction and so is protected.

Bald eagles may live as long as thirty years. They have very sharp eyes and can spot prey from great heights.

The bald eagle is brown and has white feathers on its head and tail. These white head feathers are what make the eagle look bald.

Although bald eagles once thrived throughout North America, they lived under threat of extinction for many years. Because bald eagles usually eat fish and other small animals, Alaskan hunters killed more than 100,000 bald eagles between 1917 and 1952 to protect the salmon and fur industries. Another major threat to bald eagles was the use of pesticides, such as DDT. These chemicals concentrate in the bird's body, causing it to lay infertile or thin-shelled eggs or produce deformed young. Oil spills also harm these magnificent birds of prey.

The bald eagle is now protected by federal law. In the early 1970s, the United States restricted use of DDT. As a result, the birds are on their way to making a comeback. Breeding pairs have been successfully raised in captivity and more than 1,000 bald eagles have been released into the wild. Now, the population of bald eagles is close to 40,000 in Alaska and, fortunately, its numbers are said to be steadily increasing.

BALLISTICS Ballistics is the science concerned with the motion and behavior of projectiles, such as bullets, bombs, rockets, and guided missiles. The three main branches of ballistics are interior, exterior, and terminal ballistics.

Interior ballistics deals with the motion of a projectile as it travels down the barrel of a weapon, such as a rifle or pistol. The weight of the bullet, the pressure placed on the bullet, the speed at which the bullet moves through the barrel, the barrel's length and diameter, and the speed at which the bullet leaves the barrel all affect the flight of the bullet. A person who studies the interior ballistics of a rifle or pistol has to know all these things. The interior ballistics of missiles is concerned with the design of rocket engines and the choice of propellants. A rocket is propelled by the reaction to expanding gases escaping from it.

The speed at which a projectile leaves a gun barrel or a missile leaves a launch pad is called the initial velocity. The initial velocity of the projectiles of some rifles is 5,000 ft. [1,500 m] per second. The initial velocity of missiles is lower because most missiles are much heavier than a bullet.

Exterior ballistics is concerned with the flight path, or trajectory, of a projectile from the time it leaves the rifle or gun until landing. After a bullet has left the gun, it travels in an arc, falling downward because of gravity. The amount of air resistance to a projectile depends on the projectile's size, shape, and speed, and on the density of air. Air resistance slows the projectile, reducing the range, or distance, it travels. Winds and crosswinds can affect the range and direction of a projectile. If a projectile is fired from a moving weapon, or if the target is moving, the range can be affected. Electronic computers are used to measure the effects of all these factors.

Terminal ballistics is concerned with the effect of the projectile hitting its target. Bullets cause damage by penetration. Shell or bomb damage is mainly caused by explosion, rather than by ballistic effects.

Forensic ballistics is a separate field that helps police identify bullets. Every gun or rifle makes marks on the bullets it fires. No other gun or rifle can make the same marks on a bullet. Experts can find out whether or not a particular bullet was fired from a particular gun. Forensic ballistics has greatly aided police officers in identifying and arresting armed robbers and murderers.

See also GUN; MISSILE.

BALLOON A balloon is a bag filled with hot air or a gas. A balloon rises and floats because the hot air or gas in the balloon is lighter than the air outside. Light materials, such as silk or plastic, are used in making balloons that carry passengers or materials of some kind. Such balloons may be either captive or free floating. A captive balloon is anchored to the ground by a line called a tether. A free-floating balloon travels in whatever direction the wind blows it. Many balloons have a gondola, or basket, attached below to carry passengers and equipment.

The first practical hot-air balloon was developed in France by two brothers, Joseph and Etienne Montgolfier. Their balloon was made of cloth and paper and had a diameter of about 35 ft. [11 m]. They first flew the balloon on June 5, 1783. The first people to fly in a free-floating balloon were Jean-Francois Pilâtre de Rozier and Francois Laurent, the Marquis d'Arlandes. They made their flight across Paris in November, 1783. The following month, J.A.C. Charles and Nicolas Louis Robert made the world's first flight in a hydrogen-filled balloon. They rose to about 2,000 ft. [610 m] and traveled 27 mi. [43 km].

There are two kinds of balloons—gas and hot-air. The main kinds of gas balloons are superpressure balloons, zero-pressure balloons, and expandable balloons. All three are used for scientific purposes.

In a superpressure balloon, the gas inside has a greater pressure than that of the air outside. When a superpressure balloon is launched, the bag is partly filled and then is sealed. The gas expands as the balloon rises. The bag of a superpressure balloon is not flexible, so once the bag is filled, the balloon does not go any higher. Superpressure balloons can stay in the air for many months.

The gas inside a zero-pressure balloon is at the same pressure as that of the air on the outside. Once the balloon is aloft, the gas expands. If the gas expands too much, the excess gas escapes

BALLOON—Different uses

A scientific weather balloon is about to be launched (below left). It contains special instruments to study conditions in the atmosphere. Hydrogen-filled balloons were used by Union forces during the Civil War (1861–1865) to observe Confederate troops (below right). Many of the balloons trailed telegraph wires through which their crews could communicate with troops on the ground.

BALLOON—Modern safety
Modern gas balloons and airships are filled with helium, which is much safer to use than hydrogen because it does not burn.

through a valve. In order to keep zero-pressure balloons in the air, ballast (a load of material carried just for this purpose) must be released from time to time. This is done by radio signals from the ground. Zero-pressure balloons usually fly for several days.

Expandable balloons are about 6 ft. [2 m] across when they lift off. As the balloon rises and the gas expands, the bag may expand to about 20 ft. [6 m]. When the balloon reaches the proper height, the bag bursts, and its instruments are returned to earth by parachute.

Gas balloons may be filled with hydrogen, helium, or natural gas. Natural gas is by far the cheapest, but it has the least lifting ability. Helium costs more than natural gas, but it is nonflammable (that is, it will not catch fire) and therefore very safe. Hydrogen has the greatest lifting ability, because it is the lightest gas. However, hydrogen can be dangerous because it is highly combustible (capable of catching fire).

Hot-air balloons work much the same way that gas balloons do. The air in the bag is heated, making it lighter than the air outside. The air is heated by a propane-gas burner mounted below the bag. To make the balloon rise, more propane is burned. To lose altitude, less gas is burned.

Balloons have been used in wars. For example, balloons were used by France in a war in 1870. They were also used in the Civil War, World War I, and World War II. For the most part, captive balloons were used to observe the enemy's troops.

Information about the weather is still collected by instruments carried by balloons. Weather researchers, or meteorologists, release balloons into the atmosphere to study the temperature, humidity, and pressure of the air at various altitudes. They can use this information to forecast the weather although most of the information used by weather forecasters is now supplied by satellites (see METEOROLOGY). Balloons are also sent high into the stratosphere (the second layer of the atmosphere above the earth) carrying instruments to record conditions such as cosmic radiation (see COSMIC RAYS). These balloons may also carry telescopes and cameras. They have gone up as high as 32 mi. [51.8 km].

Sport balloonists use both gas and hot-air balloons. Balloon races and rallies are held in many parts of the country. To get a ballooning license from the Federal Aviation Administration (FAA), a person must be at least 16 years old, pass a written examination, and have ten hours of flying time with an instructor.

The record for the highest flight in a helium-filled balloon was set in 1961 by two U.S. Navy officers—Commander Malcolm Ross and Lieutenant Commander Victor A. Prather, Jr. In the balloon *Lee Lewis Memorial*, they rose 113,739.9 ft. [34,668 m].

The first people to cross the Atlantic Ocean in a balloon were Maxie Anderson, Ben Abruzzo, and Larry Newman. In August 1978, in the *Double Eagle II*, they lifted off from Presque Isle, Maine. They landed in Misery, France, slightly over 137 hours later. They had traveled 3,107 mi. [5,000 km].

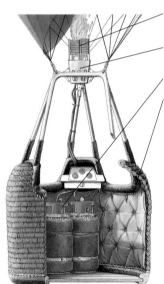

Gas burner

Control valve

Propane gas tank

Basket

BALLOON—Fuel
Modern hot-air ballons carry their own heat source, a propane gas burner. Gas from tanks in the basket is burned to heat the air in the balloon. The balloon's height is controlled by turning the burner on and off.

In June 1988, Per Linstrand of the United Kingdom set the record for the highest flight in a hot-air balloon when he rose to an altitude of 64,996 ft. [19,811 m] above Laredo, Texas.
See also AVIATION.

BALSAM (bôl′sǝm) Balsam is an aromatic resin that comes from some herbs and trees (see RESIN). Balsam is used mainly in the making of medicine, paint, perfume, and incense. Some balsams flow naturally from herbs and trees. Other balsams must be gotten by cutting or breaking open herbs and trees. In North America, Canada balsam is taken from fir trees.

BALSAM
Some South American trees (right) are a source of resin called balsam, which is purified by heating (above).

BAMBOO Bamboo is a member of the grass family, Gramineae. Bamboos are native to tropical and subtropical climates in Asia, Africa, and North America. Growing from an underground stem called a rhizome, they grow very rapidly. Most bamboos are very tall—some as high as 120 ft. [37 m]—and as thick as 1 ft. [30 cm].

BAMBOO
Bamboo is one of the grass family of plants. It has a hollow stem. Bamboo may take up to 100 years to grow to its full height of 120 feet [37 m].

Bamboos have hollow wood stems. The leaves fall off as the plant grows. Some bamboos blossom once in thirty years, while others may take one hundred years. The plant dies after it blooms. The seeds from the blossoms grow into new plants.

Bamboo is used to make many products. Some fishing poles are made from the stems of the plant. Bamboo stems are also used to make rafts, furniture, and fences. In some countries, the young stems and rhizomes are pickled and eaten as bamboo shoots.

BANANA Bananas are plants that grow in tropical regions. They grow 4 to 30 ft. [1.3 to 9 m] in height. The banana plant looks like a palm tree, but it is not a tree. It does not have a woody stem or trunk. Instead, its leaves grow from a tough rootstock by which the plant spreads.

One large flower grows from the central stalk of the plant. This flower develops into the fruit, also called a banana. Each plant has one bunch of bananas, which can weight as much as 100 lb. [45 kg]. Cultivation of the banana plant has resulted in a fruit that has no seeds. New plants are started from cuttings from old plants.

Bananas are cut while they are green. They are then loaded on trains to be transported to ships that carry them to many parts of the world.

BANANA
Bananas grow in bunches on plants in hot, damp climates, such as in parts of Central and South America.

During shipment, they begin to mature and turn yellow. Brazil is the leading banana-growing country, producing as much as 5.5 million tons [5 million metric tons] a year. The United States imports more bananas than any other country.

Bananas are a nutritious food. They contain potassium and vitamins A and C and are rich in carbohydrates. Manila hemp is made from the fibers of some banana plants. It is used to make rope and certain fabrics.

BANDICOOT
Bandicoots are marsupials that live in Australia and New Guinea. They carry and nurse their young in a pouch.

BANDICOOT (băn′dĭ kōōt′) Bandicoots make up a family of marsupials found in Australia and New Guinea (see MARSUPIAL). There are about twenty species. These ratlike mammals rarely grow to be larger than 2 ft. [0.6 m]. The second and third toes are grown together. Like all marsupials, the bandicoot carries and nurses its young in a pouch. Only the bandicoot, however, has a pouch that opens at the bottom instead of at the top. The bandicoot is nocturnal. It sleeps in a burrow during the day and comes out to eat plants and insects at night.

BANNEKER, BENJAMIN (1731–1806) Benjamin Banneker was an African-American astronomer, inventor, and mathematician. Banneker also wrote essays. He was born in Ellicott, Maryland, and was educated at a school with both black and white students. Banneker spent most of his life as a tobacco farmer. He learned astronomy and mathematics by teaching himself. When he was in his twenties, he became famous for creating the first working clock made entirely in America. Banneker carved the wheels and gears out of wood. He also published research on bees, did a mathematical study of the life of the seventeen-year locust, and wrote about the need for peace and racial equality.

Banneker is well known for his almanacs, published between 1791 and 1797, which included his astronomical calculations and observations. An almanac is a book containing information about such topics as astronomy and the weather, arranged by the days, weeks, and months of a year. Banneker contributed astronomical calculations for other almanacs until 1802. In 1791, Banneker was invited by George Washington, the first president of the United States, to help survey (measure) the land that would become the capital of the United States, now called Washington, D.C. Banneker was also helpful in planning the placement of streets and buildings in the city. Banneker was the first black to be appointed to an official position by a president.

BANTING, SIR FREDERICK GRANT
(1891–1941) Sir Frederick Banting was a Canadian physician who discovered insulin, a hormone that controls the body's use of sugar. Working with Charles Best and others, Banting discovered this hormone by taking it out of the pancreas (see INSULIN).

Banting's discovery led to a complete change in the treatment of diabetes mellitus, a disease that occurs because of either the lack of, or the body's inability to use, insulin (see DIABETES). Banting and a partner, J. J. Macleod, won the 1923 Nobel Prize for medicine for the discovery of insulin. Banting shared his prize with Charles Best, a fellow researcher, a striking example of scientific partnership.

BANYAN
The banyan is a member of the mulberry family that produces figlike fruits. It is found in tropical Asia and Africa. The banyan may grow as tall as 100 ft. [30 m]. It has roots growing down from its branches into the ground. Some banyans cover 1 acre [0.4 hectare] or more.

BANYAN

The banyan tree is found in Africa and Asia. It produces roots that grow down from its branches into the ground.

Some varieties of banyans are epiphytes that grow onto other trees in order to support their roots (see EPIPHYTE).

BARBERRY FAMILY
The barberry family is a group of about five hundred species of spiny shrubs that are dicotyledons (see DICOTYLEDON). Barberries grow from 3 to 12 ft. [1 to 3.7 m] high. Barberry shrubs are native to the moderate-

BARBERRY FAMILY

It is prohibited to grow common barberry in certain areas, since it can introduce diseases in wheat.

climate zones of the Northern Hemisphere. They are most frequently planted by landscapers for hedges and other landscape features. They have yellow wood and yellow six-petaled flowers. The berries are red, yellow, blue, purple, or black. The berries of most species can be made into jellies. A yellow dye is found in some of the barberry plants of Asia and South America.

In the United States, the best known kinds of barberries are the common barberry, the American (or Allegheny) barberry, the Japanese barberry, and also the wintergreen barberry.

The common barberry is attacked by spring stem rust, which is a fungus very harmful to wheat. For this reason, there are laws in the wheat-growing areas of the United States that prohibit the growing of barberry.

BARBITURATE (bär bĭch′ər ĭt) A barbiturate is a drug that slows down the activity of the brain and the rest of the nervous system. Barbiturates are sometimes prescribed by doctors to induce sleep, or relax and calm people, when they suffer from severe anxiety. In the United States, barbiturates can be obtained legally only with a doctor's prescription.

Barbiturates are made from barbituric acid. They come in tablet or capsule form or sometimes as a powder or liquid. Different barbiturates vary in strength and in the length of time that their effects last. Also, different people may have different reactions to taking the same amount of the same barbiturate.

Regular use of barbiturates can lead to addiction (see ADDICTION). Some people improperly take large amounts of barbiturates to escape tension. Large doses make the user's speech become slurred, and coordination and judgment become poor. A person can die from an overdose of barbiturates. When an addicted person tries to stop taking barbiturates, he or she becomes extremely nervous. His or her body may shake and twitch violently. Abruptly stopping the use of barbiturates can cause death. An addict can usually end his or her dependency on the drugs by gradually reducing the amount taken.

Today, barbiturates are used less frequently for their sleep-inducing and calming effects than are another kind of drug, called benzodiazepines. Benzodiazepines are considered safer and more effective than barbiturates. Barbiturates are now used mostly to prevent seizures from epilepsy or as anesthetics (see ANESTHETIC; EPILEPSY). Barbiturates are also occasionally used with mentally ill patients, helping to calm and relax them so they can talk over their problems with their doctors.

BARIUM (bâr′ē əm) Barium is a soft, silvery-white metallic element. It was discovered in 1808 by Sir Humphry Davy, an English scientist (see DAVY, SIR HUMPHRY; ELEMENT). Barium is found most often in a mineral called barite, or heavy spar. It is extracted from barite by electrolysis (see ELECTROLYSIS).

Barium is a very reactive metal and is almost never found in a pure state. This is because it reacts with the oxygen in the air. Pure barium has very few uses, but its compounds are widely used. Doctors use barium sulfate in X-ray examinations. The patient whose intestines will be X-rayed takes the barium sulfate by mouth or by means of an enema. The barium sulfate absorbs X rays, and the intestines show up white on the photograph. Barium nitrate is used in fireworks to give a green flame. Barium carbonate is used in ceramics and in glass.

Barium's symbol is Ba. Its atomic number is 56. Its relative atomic mass is 137.3. Barium melts at 1,337°F [725°C] and boils at 2,984°F [1,640°C]. Its relative density is 3.5 (see RELATIVE DENSITY).

BARK Bark is the protective outer covering of tree branches, trunks, and roots. Bark has three layers. The outer periderm is made mostly of dead tissue called cork. The periderm is usually thick. It protects the tree against weather, insects, and disease. The middle cortex layer is made of living but nongrowing cells. The innermost phloem carries food made in the tree's leaves down to the roots. The periderm of some trees has small openings called lenticels. Lenticels allow gases such as carbon dioxide and oxygen to enter and leave the plant.

People use bark mainly for its cork. Quinine, cough medicine, cinnamon, and other useful substances are also obtained from bark.

See also CORK; CORTEX; PHLOEM; QUININE.

BARK

The bark of some trees is valuable. Cinnamon, a spice that has been used since ancient times, is made from the bark of the cinnamon tree (above). Bark helps protect trees. For example, the thick bark of slash pines helps insulate the trees from the heat of forest fires.

ACTIVITY *Bark rubbing*

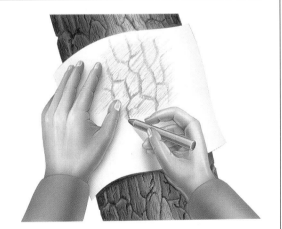

One way to compare the bark of different trees is by making bark rubbings. Hold a thin white sheet of paper against the trunk and carefully rub the paper with a wax crayon. A pattern of the bark will be left on the paper.

BARLEY Barley is a widely used cereal plant of the genus *Hordeum*. This genus, having 16 species, is a member of the grass family. Barleys are found in Europe, Asia, northern Africa, and North America. Barley heads usually have long, bristly flowers that grow in tightly bunched spikes, with three additional spikes at each node (see NODE). Most barleys are considered weeds. One species, called squirrel tail grass, is grown for use as an ornament. Barley grown as a crop comes from three species, with two, four, or six rows of grain on the spike. Such barley is used as animal feed, to make malt for use in such products as beer and malted milk, as an ingredient in soups, and to make flour for use in cereal and bread.

Barley thrives in cool climates. In warmer climates, barley is planted as a winter crop. Spring barley is planted in spring and matures by summer. Winter barley is planted in fall and harvested the next summer. The grain should be harvested when it is dry enough so that a kernel snaps when bitten. Barley can be grown in the same place for many years if the soil is properly fed and if the barley does not succumb to diseases or soil erosion. Russia is the world's largest producer of barley.

BARLEY

Barley is a cereal plant belonging to the grass family. It grows in most countries of the Northern Hemisphere, either as a spring or a winter crop.

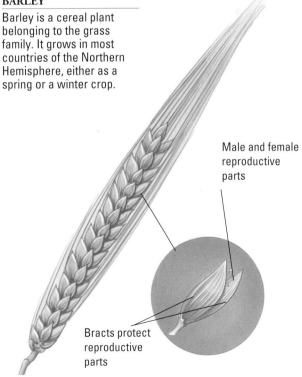

Male and female reproductive parts

Bracts protect reproductive parts

BARNACLE Barnacles are saltwater crustaceans that spend their entire adult lives attached to underwater objects (see CRUSTACEAN). Barnacles have been found on rocks, turtles, whales, buoys, and ship bottoms. There are about eight hundred species of barnacles. Most grow a hard, chalky covering around themselves for protection. This covering has an opening for the barnacle's legs. Barnacles capture microscopic organisms for food by waving their legs out of this opening. The motion of their legs also brings dissolved oxygen into the shell. When in danger, the barnacle pulls its legs inside the shell and hides.

Barnacles have three life stages. In the first, they are small, free-swimming creatures with one eye. In the second stage, they have six pairs of legs, two eyes, and two feelers. In the third stage, they still have twelve legs, but they lose their eyes. They attach themselves to underwater objects during this stage.

Barnacles that attach themselves to the bottoms of ships cause serious problems. They slow the ships by increasing the ships' resistance to the water. They also add weight. Barnacles may increase the weight of an ocean liner by several tons. This is known as the fouling problem.

BARNARD, CHRISTIAAN NEETHLING (1922–) Dr. Christiaan Barnard is a South African surgeon who performed the first human heart transplant operation. On December 3, 1967, in the Groote Schuur hospital in Cape Town, South Africa, he transplanted a heart into 55-year-old Louis Washkansky. The heart had belonged to a 25-year-old woman who had died in an automobile accident. Washkansky lived for 18 days but finally died of a lung infection. Barnard has since performed many such operations. In 1974, he transplanted a human heart into a patient without removing the patient's own heart. He joined the donor heart to the patient's heart, providing a "double pump" for the circulatory system. Barnard also experimented with transplanting animal hearts into human beings. *See also* HEART; TRANSPLANTATION.

BAROMETER A barometer is a device that measures atmospheric, or air, pressure. It is used to help forecast the weather and to measure the altitude, or height, of objects and areas above sea level.

In 1643, an Italian, Evangelista Torricelli, showed that when a tube sealed at one end was filled with mercury and turned upside down into a bowl of mercury, the mercury in the tube did not all flow out. It fell only until its top was at a certain height. The weight of air pressing down

BAROMETER
Inside an aneroid barometer is a disk-shaped metal chamber containing a vacuum (aneroid means "without air"). As the pressure of the surrounding air changes, the chamber is squeezed more or less strongly. The changes in its shape cause a pointer to move. The pointer moves over a scale that shows the atmospheric pressure. The scale is marked both in inches of mercury and in millibars.

on the mercury in the bowl held the mercury in the tube at that height. Torricelli was able to show that average air pressure at sea level balances a column of mercury 30 in. [76 cm] high. (The diameter of the mercury column does not matter.)

Other scientists then reasoned that altitude could be measured by observing changes in the height of the mercury at different locations. Because air is thinner at great heights, they believed its pressure would be less and would support less mercury as height increased. The higher above sea level, the lower the column of mercury would be. This was proved to be true. Today, barometers are used in airplanes to measure altitude. These barometers, called altimeters, do not use mercury (see ALTIMETER).

In a mercury barometer, a printed scale beside the tube containing mercury gives the barometric reading, or measurement. It may be written in inches or millimeters or in units called bars and millibars. In 1939, the United States Weather Bureau adopted the bar as a unit of measurement. It gives a more exact pressure reading at sea level of 29.53 in. [75.01 cm]. One millibar is one-thousandth of a bar, and is the pressure that balances a column of mercury 0.03 in. [0.08 cm] high.

A mercury barometer is used for weather forecasting. When the mercury drops rapidly, a storm is forecast. When the mercury rises steadily, good weather is forecast.

Aneroid barometers use no liquid. They show air pressure by recording its effect on an airtight box that has had some of its air taken out. The sides of the box move in and out according to the amount of air pressure on them. The movements of the sides are recorded by a pointer, which moves across a scale. Aneroid barometers are smaller than mercury barometers and easier to carry.

The barograph is an aneroid barometer that scientists use to keep records of changes in air pressure. The barograph records air pressure on paper that is attached to a revolving drum.

See also ATMOSPHERE; ATMOSPHERE (UNIT); MILLIBAR; WEATHER.   PROJECT 22, 25, 26

BARRACUDA

The barracuda is a saltwater fish belonging to the family Sphyraenidae. It is a long, slender fish with many large, sharp teeth. Barracuda are found in coastal waters of warm seas throughout the world. There are five species of barracuda in North American waters. The great barracuda, which lives off the coast of Florida, may reach lengths of 8 ft. [2.5 m]. The barracuda is considered dangerous, and instances have been recorded of this fish attacking swimmers.

BARRACUDA

Blackfin barracuda are found above the Great Barrier Reef, off the northeast coast of Australia. Barracuda form groups called schools, in which they hunt and kill smaller fish.

BASALT

(bə sôlt′) Basalt is a heavy, black or gray igneous rock made of tiny grains (see IGNEOUS ROCK). The grains are crystals, usually made of the minerals plagioclase and pyroxene. Basalt is formed from lava, the red-hot liquid from volcanoes. Basalt is the most common volcanic rock. Hawaii, Samoa, and Tahiti are volcanic islands formed of basalt.

When lava cools and hardens to form basalt, the basalt can split into columns, with a surface resembling giant stepping stones. Cliffs having basalt columns are among famous tourist attractions. One is the Devil's Postpile in California; another is the Giant's Causeway in Northern

BASALT

Basalt is an igneous rock that solidified from lava. It consists mainly of tiny grains, but it can contain large crystals of particular minerals.

Ireland. Some large basalt fields have been built by lava flowing from narrow openings in the ground. On the Columbia Plateau, a basalt field in the state of Washington, the basalt is about 3,300 ft. [1,000 m] or more thick. Crushed basalt is used to make roads and as building stone.
See also ROCK; VOLCANO.

BASE In chemistry, a base is often described as a compound that can combine with an acid to form a salt. Acids produce hydrogen ions (H^+) when they are dissolved in water or other solvents. Bases produce basic ions that combine with hydrogen ions. The most common basic ion is the hydroxyl ion $(OH)^-$ (see ACID; COMPOUND; IONS AND IONIZATION).

Most bases contain atoms of a metal and one or more hydroxyl (OH^-) groups. These bases are formed when a metal oxide reacts with water (see OXIDATION AND REDUCTION). Bases in water solution taste bitter and feel slippery. They turn red litmus paper blue. In a solution, bases ionize, or break down, into positive and negative ions. A strong base, such as sodium hydroxide (NaOH), breaks down almost completely in solution (see SOLUTION AND SOLUBILITY). Such bases are called alkalis (see ALKALI). A weak base, such as ammonium hydroxide (NH_4OH), ionizes (breaks down) only slightly in water. Bases have a pH from 7 to 14. The stronger the base, the higher the pH number.

The bases sodium hydroxide (caustic soda) and potassium hydroxide (caustic potash) are used in making soap, paper, bleach, and many kinds of chemicals. Along with ammonium hydroxide, or ammonia solution, they are useful cleaning agents because they cause reactions that remove grease. Calcium oxide (quicklime) is used to make glass, and calcium hydroxide (slaked lime) to make mortar.
See also NEUTRALIZATION.

PROJECT 1

BASE CODE In biology, a base is a substance that helps the nucleic acid within a cell store information (see NUCLEIC ACID). The base code is a set of chemical instructions within the nucleic acid, which controls how the cell makes the proteins it needs.

Each kind of nucleic acid has four kinds of bases, which can be thought of as "letters" in the base code. A molecule of DNA contains a very long sequence of bases, arranged in a particular order (see DNA). This order makes up the base code, also called the genetic code.

The smallest units used in the base code (we can call them "letters") are joined up to make longer units (which we can call "words"). Each of these "words" is three bases long, and each "word" has a precise meaning to the cell. Most of the base code "words" control where a particular amino acid is incorporated into a protein chain, while others show where a chain of amino acids should start or stop (see AMINO ACID). Since there are four kinds of bases altogether, and they can be arranged in 64 different groups of three, there are more than enough combinations to specify which of the twenty kinds of amino acids join together to make all the proteins in a living thing.

BASKET STAR The basket star is a marine echinoderm. It is a member of the class Ophiuroidea (see ECHINODERMATA). The basket star gets its name from its star-shaped body and its five long arms. Each of these arms branches off into other arms, making this organism look like a basket. The arms are used to gather debris to be eaten as food. It lives on the ocean floor.
See also BRITTLE STAR.

BASKET STAR
Basket stars are marine animals related to starfish. The basket star has a star-shaped body.

BASS Bass is the name given to several kinds of fish. True basses are saltwater fishes belonging to the Percichthyidae and Serranidae families. Well-known examples are the striped bass, channel bass, and grouper.

Better known, however, are the freshwater basses. They belong to the sunfish family, Centrarchidae. The largemouth bass and small-mouth bass are especially popular game fishes. The fishes were originally found in only some areas of North America. They have since been taken to waters in every state and to many countries around the world. The world's record large-mouth bass weighed 24 lb., 4 oz. [10.9 kg]. It was caught in the state of Georgia.

BASS
The largemouth bass lives in streams and lakes throughout North America. It has two dorsal fins on its back.

BAT Bats are the only mammals that can fly. Their wings are actually long arms and fingers covered with a thin skin that connects down the body to the lower legs. Like other mammals, bats have legs, but they do not walk on them. They depend almost entirely on flying, using their legs and feet when they hang upside down in a roosting position.

Bats are furry animals, many of which look somewhat like mice. They vary in size. The smallest have bodies 1.5 in. [3.8 cm] long with a wingspread of about 6 in. [15 cm]. The largest may be 12 in. [30 cm] long and have a wingspread of 6 ft. [1.8 m]. Some bats, depending on the shape and length of their wings, can fly as fast as 32 m.p.h. [51 kph]. The smaller ones fly around 5 to 8 m.p.h. [8 to 13 kph].

Nearly all bats have nocturnal habits, sleeping during the day and flying at night in search of food. They live together in colonies of between a few dozen and hundreds of thousands, and roost in trees and caves. Many species feed on insects. By eating insects that people consider pests, bats are beneficial to humankind.

A very interesting part of bat behavior is how they navigate at night in search of food. Although they have good vision and see well in dim light, they fly and locate food in the dark by using a system called echolocation. They send out very high sounds in the form of short bursts. The sounds are too high-pitched for human beings to hear. The sounds bounce off objects and return as echoes, helping the animals determine the direction and distance of anything in their paths. Bats can detect and catch insects in the air. Experiments in the laboratory show they are even able to locate and avoid hitting very fine wires strung in their way. This system of echolocation is similar to, and in fact helped lead to the development of, the sonar and radar systems developed by

BAT
The flying fox, or fruit bat, uses its eyes to navigate and find food. It feeds mainly on fruit, but also on flowers and nectar.

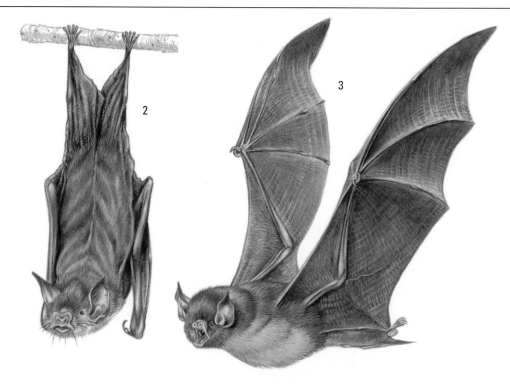

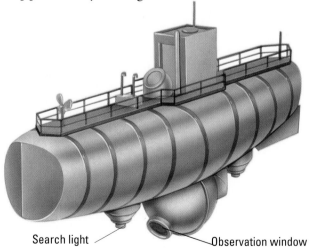

BAT

Bats are flying mammals. Many species navigate by using sound waves. These include: (1) the Mexican funnel-eared bat, (2) Davy's naked-backed bat, and (3) the Honduran disk-winged bat.

people for navigation under the sea and in the air.

Bats usually mate in the fall. The young are born in the spring. The females may have from one to four babies a year, depending on the kind of bat. Because bats do not build nests, infant bats must cling to their mothers for several weeks. During this time, the young are given thorough training in flying and hunting.

There are many species of bats living all over the world. The most common kinds to be found in North America are the brown bats, the Mexican free-tailed bats, the hoary bats, and the silver-haired bats. A common kind found in Central and South America is the vampire bat. It is known especially for its unique habit of feeding on the blood of other animals, mainly cattle. The vampire bat digs into the skin of its prey with sharp bites, then licks the blood from the wound. The vampire bat drinks about 1.5 oz. [15 ml], or about one tablespoon, of blood each day. However, vampire bats are dangerous to people and animals only if they carry the disease rabies.

BATHYSPHERE AND BATHYSCAPHE

A bathysphere (băth′ĭ sfîr′) is a hollow steel ball with portholes, once used for deep-sea exploring. It is large enough to hold one person inside. The bathysphere was designed by Otis Barton, an American. It was used in the 1930s and 1940s to go down as far as 3,300 ft. [1,000 m] under the sea. The bathysphere, attached to a ship by a cable, was always being knocked around as the ship was tossed about on the waves.

The bathyscaphe (băth′ĭ skăf′) was designed to overcome this problem. It was invented by Auguste Piccard, a Swiss scientist, who was famous for his balloon flights (see PICCARD, AUGUSTE). The bathyscaphe is free-floating. It is supported by a large float tank filled with

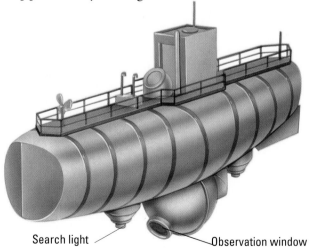

Search light — Observation window

BATHYSCAPHE

The crew compartment of this bathyscaphe is the sphere that is just visible beneath the huge gasoline-filled tank. Gasoline is less dense than water, and its purpose is not to power the engines but to make the vessel float.

gasoline. Piccard started work in 1939. In 1948, he dived in his bathyscaphe *FNRS* to a depth of more than 5,000 ft. [1,524 m]. His later, improved bathyscaphe, *Trieste*, was bought by the United States Navy. The *Trieste* went down 35,800 ft. [10,912 m] into the Mariana Trench in the Pacific in 1960.

Research and development programs for deep-diving vehicles have continued. Their goals are related to national defense, the need for services such as search and rescue, salvage operations, and the promise of new resources from the ocean.

BATTERY A battery is a device that produces electricity by chemical action. A battery contains one or more units called cells. Each cell can produce electric current. Single cell batteries are used to power flashlights and toys. Batteries with several cells provide electricity for automobiles, heavy equipment, spacecraft, submarines, and emergency electric lights.

The first battery was developed in the late 1790s by Count Alessandro Volta, an Italian scientist (see VOLTA, ALESSANDRO). In 1859, a French physicist, Gaston Plante, invented the first lead-acid storage battery. Another French scientist, Georges Leclanché, introduced the first dry cell battery a few years later.

Primary, or dry cell, batteries do not have long lives. They stop giving off electricity when their chemicals lose their power. These batteries usually consist of one cell. Secondary, or wet cell, batteries can be used for years. They can be recharged many times after they are first discharged. They usually consist of several cells.

Batteries come in many sizes. Tiny ones used to power electric watches and hearing aids weigh as little as 0.05 oz. [1.4 g]. Huge batteries used in submarines weigh up to 1 ton [0.91 metric ton]. The average automobile storage battery weighs about 35 to 40 lb. [16 to 18 kg].

Batteries differ in voltage, or strength. A typical flashlight battery produces 1½ volts.

Dry cell batteries Millions of dry cell batteries are manufactured each year. They contain rodlike structures called electrodes. A thick, pastelike chemical substance that can conduct electricity, called an electrolyte, surrounds the electrodes (see ELECTRODE). The zinc casings of dry cells also act as electrodes. Chemical reaction between the electrolyte and the electrodes creates an electric charge, or voltage difference, between the electrodes. When a device is attached to the electrodes, the current flows from one electrode to the other, making the device work.

There are three main types of dry cell batteries: carbon-zinc, alkaline, and mercury. The carbon-zinc battery was developed first. Most flashlight batteries are of the carbon-zinc type. The rodlike electrode is made of carbon. The other electrode is the zinc casing. The electrolyte consists of ammonium chloride, zinc chloride, and water. Carbon-zinc batteries can be recharged. However, the charge only lasts a short time.

An alkaline dry cell battery is more powerful. It lasts five to eight times longer than a carbon-zinc battery. It has a carbon electrode and a zinc casing electrode. The electrolyte is a strong alkali solution, potassium hydroxide (see ALKALI). Alkaline dry cells are used mainly for portable radios.

In a mercury dry cell, the voltage remains constant to the end of the battery's life. A mercuric oxide electrode is used. The other electrode is the zinc casing. The electrolyte is potassium hydroxide. Mercury dry cells can be made in the form of small disks for use in pocket calculators, hearing aids, watches, and so on.

BATTERY—Alkaline

These are all alkaline batteries, designed to be used to power items such as toys, radios, and other domestic products.

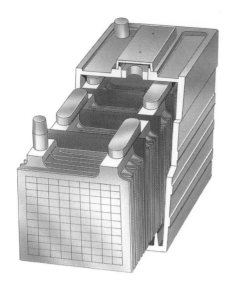

BATTERY—Lead acid

This lead-acid automobile battery contains six cells, each with six lead plates dipping into sulfuric acid. The plates are alternately negatively and positively charged. The positive plates of one cell are connected to each other and to the negative plates of the next cell, giving a total voltage of about 12 volts.

Wet cell batteries

Wet cell batteries Wet cell, or storage, batteries produce much more electricity than dry cell batteries. They are large in size and can be recharged many times. There are two main types of storage batteries: lead-acid and nickel-cadmium.

Lead-acid batteries consist of plastic or hard rubber containers with three or six cells. Each cell contains two sets of electrodes. One set is positive. The other set is negative. The electrolyte is a mixture of sulfuric acid and water. Chemical reaction causes an electric charge to build up at the electrodes. Most automobile storage batteries contain six cells that generate a total of 12 volts. Such a battery is charged by passing electricity through it. When in operation, electrons flow from the negative pole to the positive pole. A recent development in lead-acid batteries is the maintenance-free battery. It does not require the periodic addition of water. It lasts longer because its electrodes are made of alloys containing lead, calcium, and tin. Unlike the electrodes in regular lead-acid batteries, these electrodes do not cause the battery to discharge, or lose its power, when it is not in use.

Nickel-cadmium storage batteries operate on the same general principles as lead-acid batteries but contain a different electrolyte and different electrodes. The electrolyte is a solution of potassium hydroxide. The positive electrodes are made of nickel oxide, and the negative electrodes are made of cadmium. Nickel-cadmium batteries can be sealed airtight. They do not require periodic additions of water. This makes them ideal for use in portable tools and equipment and in space satellites.

See also ELECTRICITY; FUEL CELL. **PROJECT 29, 30**

BAUD Baud is a measure of the speed per second at which an electronic signal travels between computers. One baud is equal to the transmission of one bit per second. *Bit* refers to a unit of information. As the baud rate increases, communication occurs faster. Personal computers usually transmit information at a rate of 300 to 2,400 baud. PCs are now capable of baud rates up to 19,200, but usually use the slower rates because these match the rates used by most common communications devices.

See also COMPUTER.

BAUXITE Bauxite is the ore from which aluminum, the most abundant metal in the earth's crust, is extracted (see ORE). Bauxite is white, unless it has been stained red or brown by iron.

BAUXITE

Bauxite being mined in Jamaica is shown. Bauxite is the ore that is the source of aluminum.

Most bauxite is hard and rocklike, but some is soft like clay.

Bauxite is usually found in areas where the climate is hot and moist. For example, large deposits of bauxite are found in Arkansas, Alabama, and Georgia. Bauxite is also used to make alum, a white mineral salt found in some baking powders and cosmetics. Bauxite also may be mixed with clay to make bricks. These bricks line furnaces that melt steel. Bauxite is also combined with sulfuric acid to make aluminum sulfate, a chemical used in the paper, textile, and dye industries. *See also* ALUM; ALUMINUM.

BAYBERRY The bayberry is a West Indian tree. Its leaves produce bay oil. Bay oil is used in making perfumes and bay rum. This tree is also called the wild cinnamon tree.

The name *bayberry* is also given to a shrub belonging to the family Myricaceae, found along the North American seacoasts. Its bark can be used to make a liquid that is used in medicine. Upon boiling, its grayish, waxy berries yield myrtle wax, which is used in making bayberry candles.

BAYBERRY
The young shoots of the bayberry, or wild cinnamon tree are tinged with red. As they age, they become green.

BEADLE, GEORGE WELLS (1903–1989) George Wells Beadle was an American scientist who worked in the field of genetics. In 1958, he and his co-worker, Edward L. Tatum, won the Nobel Prize for medicine for discoveries that helped explain how genes work. Beadle used a form of bread mold. By using X rays on the mold, he was able to show that irradiated molds have different chemical changes in their enzymes from molds that have not been irradiated. His experiments proved that genes control the making of enzymes.
See also ENZYME; GENE; GENETICS; IRRADIATION.

BEAK A beak is a pair of jaws without teeth, found in all birds. It is also the name used to describe the jaws of an octopus.

Birds use their beaks mainly to collect and eat their food, but also to preen, build nests, and defend themselves. Some birds, such as parrots, even use them to help climb trees. A bird's beak is made of bone covered by a layer of horn, which is the same substance found in hair and fingernails. Once the bird is adult, the bone usually stops growing, but the horn grows continuously, so that it can be replaced as it wears out.

Each particular species of bird has a beak suited for the food it eats (see ADAPTATION).

BEAK
The sicklebill vanga uses its long, curved beak to probe under rotting wood for insects. The bird catches its prey in its beak. It then holds big prey with its feet and uses its bill to pull the insect into pieces ready to eat.

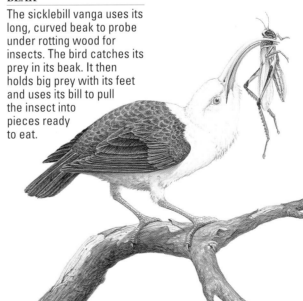

BEAN The bean plant is a member of the pea family (see PEA FAMILY). Several different types of beans are grown widely for human use or animal feed. Beans vary in size, color, and tenderness.

The most important type of bean grown in the United States is the soybean. Other types include the scarlet runner bean and the kidney bean. The lima bean is grown mainly in Central America and the midwestern United States.

The bean plant grows as a shrub or as a tall climbing vine. Before the beans are ready to be picked, the plant usually has brightly colored flowers. The bean plant grows best in warm, moist climates.

ACTIVITY   *Germinating beans*

Collect a large glass jar, several paper towels, and several beans, such as black beans or lima beans. Place the paper towels along the sides of the glass jar. Now place two or three beans between the paper towels and the glass. Add 1 in. [2.5 cm] water and leave the jar in a warm place. Watch the roots and shoots grow as the beans germinate.

BEAR Bears belong to the family Ursidae. They are the largest carnivores (meat eaters) on land. Most bears live north of the equator. No wild bears live in Antarctica, Africa, or Australia.

BEAR
Bears are the largest meat-eating animals that live on dry land. A sun bear is pictured.

Although they are adapted for eating meat, most bears also eat plants. Bears have large, heavy, fur-covered bodies and short, strong legs. Each paw has five toes. Each of these toes ends in a long, heavy claw. These claws are always exposed and are used for feeding, digging, and fighting. The bottoms of the paws are hairless. Bears range in size from the sun bear at 66 lb. [30 kg] to the Alaskan brown bear at 1,700 lb. [780 kg].

Bears have small, weak eyes. Although their hearing is good, they rely almost entirely on their sense of smell. Bears have 42 teeth. Some are for tearing meat, and others are for chewing it. All bears, even tame ones, are very protective. They will often attack any person or animal that threatens them, their food, their homes, or their cubs. Bears are able to run and swim quickly.

In spite of what many people think, bears do not hibernate (see HIBERNATION). Before the winter, they gain weight and find a cave or other suitable shelter. They sleep fitfully during the winter months. They may even wake up and wander around on warm days. Bears usually live alone. They never travel in groups. A male bear will stay with a female for about a month. Shortly after mating, the male leaves. The female is then left alone to find shelter for herself and her unborn cubs. Two cubs are usually born during the winter. Some females may give birth to as many as four cubs. The cubs are born hairless and weigh less than 1 lb. [0.5 kg]. They stay with the mother for between 18 months and two years. During this time, the mother teaches them to hunt and to care for themselves.

BEARING A bearing is the part of a machine that supports a moving part, reducing the friction, or rubbing, as much as possible. Bearings are made from a metal that is softer than that of the moving part. Bearings wear out faster than the moving parts but are easier to replace. Many bearings are lined with a soft metal called Babbitt metal.

The most common types of bearings are the ball and roller bearings. These bearings depend on the principle that rolling produces much less friction than sliding. The revolving pivot, or journal, inside a ball bearing works upon a number of smaller steel balls. The balls roll easily in a track called the race. These balls are in a frame that keeps them apart from each other but allows contact with the moving parts of the machine. Roller bearings are similar but have rollers shaped like cylinders or tapered cones instead of balls. The rollers usually lie side by side around the shaft.

A plain, or oil-film, bearing consists of a soft metal shell. A plain bearing is often called a sleeve bearing, because it fits around a shaft within a machine like a coat sleeve. A film of oil covers both the bearing and the shaft to help reduce friction. The bearing is usually made of Babbitt metal, but copper and lead alloys are also widely used. Nylon bearings are used for much lighter load work. Friction between plastics and metal is quite low, and water can be used as a lubricant.

Some machines, such as refrigerator motors, use self-lubricating bearings because the machine cannot be lubricated after assembly. The jewel bearing, used in some watches and airplane instruments, has a pivot often made of crystal or a gemstone, such as ruby.

BEAUFORT SCALE The Beaufort (bō′fərt) scale is a system of describing the speed of winds based on observations. Rear Admiral Sir Francis Beaufort of the British navy created the scale in 1805. It was originally used at sea but has been changed so that it may now be used on land as well.

A person can learn the approximate speed of the wind from the scale by noticing the wind's effects. For example, a wind that begins to break twigs off trees is a fresh gale with the Beaufort number 8. A more exact, objective measure of wind speed is now found by using instruments.

See also ANEMOMETER.

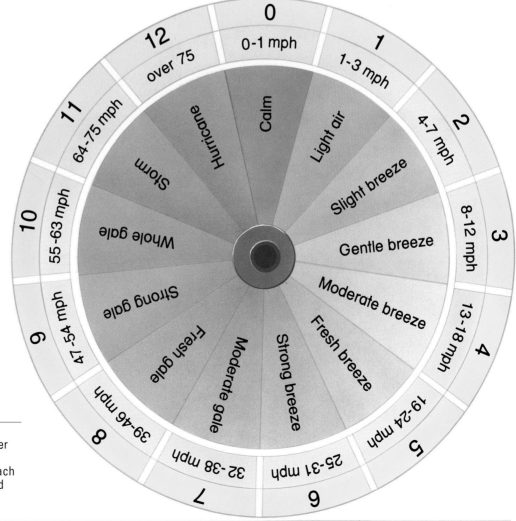

BEAUFORT SCALE

This diagram shows the Beaufort scale. The outer number is the Beaufort number, and beneath each number is the speed and description of the wind.

BEAVER—Lodge

Beavers live in lodges built of logs and branches that they gather. They construct dams across streams, ditches, and creeks and then build the lodges in the ponds that the dams create.

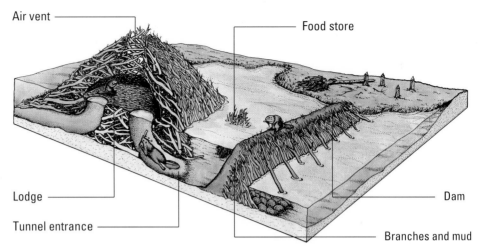

Air vent

Food store

Lodge

Dam

Tunnel entrance

Branches and mud

BEAVER The beaver is a rodent with a large, thickset body and short, strong legs (see RODENT). The beaver's hind feet are webbed for swimming. The forefeet do not have webs. The beaver uses its forefeet almost like hands. Its tail is broad and flat like a paddle and is of great use in swimming. The beaver's body can reach a length of 4 ft. [120 cm] and can weigh as much as 65 lb. [30 kg].

Beavers are aquatic animals. They live in and around lakes and streams and are common in the northern United States and in Canada. Observers of the behavior of the beaver are impressed with the animal's ability to build dams, lodges, and canals. Beavers have been called the engineers of the animal kingdom.

Beavers build dams across creeks, ditches, and streams to form artificial ponds. They build their homes, called lodges, in these ponds. If the stream is quiet, they build the dam straight across it. If the stream has a strong current, they bow the dam in an inward curve so it can stand the pressure of the water.

Dams are built out of parts of trees cut down by the beavers with their sharp teeth. The animals float logs, limbs, and twigs of the trees into place where the dam is to be built. They interweave the limbs and twigs together and cover the structure with a mortar of clay and dead leaves. Beavers start their dams during the summer months when the level of the water is lowest. They continue construction until the first cold weather. They constantly repair the dams.

The lodges are built on the banks of the lake, in shallow areas in ponds, or on small islands. They look like large mud heaps but are constructed just like the dams. The beavers enter the inside of the lodge through a tunnel that comes up from below the level of the water. They use a second tunnel to bring in food for the winter.

In a Canadian national park, during a period of 15 months, two beavers cut down 226 trees; built three dams, each 50 ft. [15 m] wide, across a river; constructed a lodge of 1,000 cu. ft. [28 cu. m]; and stored up bark, roots, and twigs for winter food in a pile of 720 cu. ft. [20 cu. m].

Beavers live together in families. The females have litters of two to four kits that stay with the families until they are two years old. They then go out to mate and start families of their own.

At one time, millions of beavers lived in North

BEAVER—Building activity

The Canadian beaver pictured is building its lodge. The beaver uses its sharp front teeth to bite off short side branches. It will then use its front paws to move the log into position.

America. They were hunted for their valuable fur until laws were passed to protect them. Now, because they are protected, the number of beavers has greatly increased in some parts of the United States.

BECQUEREL, ANTOINE HENRI
(1852–1908) Henri Becquerel (bĕ krĕl') was a French physicist who discovered radioactivity. Becquerel's grandfather had made several important discoveries in electrochemistry. His father worked with fluorescence and phosphorescence. Becquerel also worked with fluorescent substances, trying to find out if they gave off X rays. At one time, he accidentally placed some crystals of the mineral pitchblende next to some photographic film in a drawer. Later, he noticed that rays affecting the film were coming from an element in the pitchblende. This radioactive element was uranium. Becquerel showed his discovery to Marie Curie, who called the occurrence "radio activity." This led Curie to the discovery of radium, another radioactive element found in pitchblende. In 1903, Becquerel shared with Marie Curie and her husband Pierre the Nobel Prize in physics.
See also CURIE FAMILY; FLUORESCENCE; PHOSPHORESCENCE; RADIOACTIVITY.

BEDBUG
Bedbugs are small insects that feed on the blood of humans and other animals. The bedbug pierces the skin of its victim with its sharp beak. Then it sucks up blood. Some humans suffer swelling and itching from the bites of bedbugs (see PARASITE).

Bedbugs are about 0.25 in. [6 mm] long and reddish brown. They have wings that are too small for flying. They usually come out at night. During the day, they hide in bedding, furniture, cracks in the wall, or under the floor. The adult

BEDBUG

The bedbug is a parasite that is active at night. During the day it hides in bedding, furniture, walls, and floors.

bedbug lays between 100 and 250 eggs. The eggs hatch in about two weeks. Bedbugs live as long as a year. The insects can be controlled with insecticides.

BEDROCK
Bedrock is the solid rocky layer of the earth's crust that lies just below the surface. The upper part of the crust consists mainly of sedimentary rocks. Igneous and metamorphic rocks are found just under the sedimentary rocks (see ROCK). Igneous and metamorphic rocks form the solid bedrock. Movements within the earth can force bedrock above the sedimentary layer. Bedrock underlies the surface of some mountains (see MOUNTAIN). Mountainous areas can also have bedrock exposed at the surface. A section of exposed bedrock is called outcrop.
See also EARTH.

BEE—Honeybee
A honeybee worker collects nectar from a flower.

BEE
Bees are insects that belong to the order Hymenoptera. They are related to ants and wasps. There are many species of bees found all over the world. The body of a bee, which is seldom longer than 1.5 in. [3.75 cm], has three parts: a head, a thorax, and an abdomen (see ABDOMEN; THORAX). Two pairs of wings are attached to the thorax. Female bees have an organ called an ovipositor at the end of their abdomen. They use the ovipositor to lay eggs and to sting enemies.

Bees collect a sugary solution called nectar from flowers. They produce honey from the nectar. Honey is their major source of food. While the bee is collecting the nectar, it may carry pollen from one flower to another. This results in pollination of the flower. Pollination is part of sexual reproduction in plants, so bees help perform a necessary task in nature (see POLLINATION).

Hatching bees undergo a metamorphosis, or series of changes (see METAMORPHOSIS). The larva hatches and turns into a pupa, which changes into an adult bee. The larva, pupa, and adult all look different.

There are solitary bees and social bees. There are many more kinds of solitary bees than there are

BEE—Mining bee
A hairy-legged mining bee digs its burrow in sandy soil.

kinds of social bees. Most solitary bees live alone. When they do live together, they do not divide up the work in the hive as social bees do. Some solitary bees, like the carpenter bee, make their nests in wood. Most build their nests underground. Each female solitary bee builds her own nest. It has many cells, or holes, in it. The bee puts honey and nectar in the cells and then lays an egg in each one. After covering the cells, she leaves to build other nests. The honey in the cells provides food for the young bees that hatch from the eggs.

Social bees live together in large numbers. Their nests are called hives. Some social bees, like the honeybee, build their hives in dead trees. Social bees divide up their work. Different kinds of bees do different kinds of jobs.

Bumblebees One of the better-known social bees is the bumblebee. It belongs to the family Apidae. It has a thick, hairy body, sometimes reaching 1.5 in. [3.75 cm] in length. It is colored

with yellow and black stripes. A queen bumblebee moves into holes or abandoned animal nests in the spring and prepares a cell from the wax within her body. She then collects some pollen, puts it in the cell, and deposits her eggs on it. Like a bird, she sits on the eggs, protecting them from the chill of the early spring weather. The eggs hatch into worker bees who take over the building and enlarging of the nest. The worker bees are female bees unable to mate with males. The colony grows until there are a few hundred bees, but some colonies contain up to two thousand bees. Toward the end of the summer, the queen lays eggs that hatch into males and queen bees. The new queen bees mate with the males. A few weeks later, all the bees die except the queen bees. They hibernate for the winter and start building new nests in the spring.

Honeybees Another social bee is the honeybee, which also belongs to the family Apidae. This bee's body is dark brown with yellow bands. The honeybee is about 0.5 in. [1.2 cm] long. Honeybees build their hives in tree hollows or in cracks in the walls of barns.

There is usually a lot of activity around the hives of honeybees. When the food supply is low, many bees must go out to gather a new supply. When food is plentiful, some of the bees remain

BEE—Swarm
When a queen bee leaves a hive, she takes many thousands of other bees with her to start a new colony. If the queen lands on a branch of a tree the other bees will gather around her in a swarm (above). It would be extremely dangerous for you to disturb the bees in this state.

BEE—Signals

Honeybees can fly several miles in search of pollen and nectar. When a worker bee finds plants in flower, she returns to the hive and performs a sort of dance that tells the hive members where to find food. The speed and angle of the dance give the other bees information about the food's precise location. The round dance (right) indicates food is close by. A waggle dance (left) means food is farther away.

behind. They continually inspect their hives to make sure everything is in order. They make sure that it is kept in good repair. Bees returning with pollen and nectar let the other bees know where to find the food supply by doing special dancelike movements. The movements show how far away and in what direction from the hive the food can be found.

Domesticated honeybees, kept for production of honey, are called domestic bees. They are kept in wooden hives, which can be enlarged as the colony grows. Beekeepers remove honey from the hives during the summer, being careful to leave enough so that the bees can survive the winter.

Social classes among honeybees
The honeybee society has three main divisions: the workers, who provide food and protection for the colony; the queen, who lays the eggs; and the drones, who mate with the queen. An average honeybee hive contains one queen, one hundred drones, and sixty thousand workers.

The workers are female bees. They are the smallest bees in the hive. They can lay eggs but cannot mate, so the eggs are never fertilized. Each worker has a barbed stinger at the back end of the abdomen. When a bee stings another insect, it can withdraw its stinger without harm to itself. However, when a bee stings a human or other large animal, the barbs on the stinger stick under the animals' skin. A part of the bee's abdomen is pulled off when the bee tries to withdraw its stinger. The bee then dies.

BEE—Queen

The queen bee (the largest bee, light brown in color) produces many thousands of eggs during her 4- to 5-year lifetime. The eggs are fertilized by male bees, the drones. The queen is fed by the female bees, the workers.

For the first two weeks of a worker's adult life, she acts as a nurse. She feeds the queen, the drones, and the larvae. From the sixth day to the fourteenth day of her life, she secretes a substance called royal jelly from her mouth. Royal jelly is used to feed the larvae. When the worker is 14 days old, she begins to produce wax from glands on the underside of her abdomen. She uses this wax to build the cells that form the structure called the honeycomb. When a worker is three weeks old, she joins in the search for pollen and nectar. She also cleans the hive and stands guard at the hive's entrance.

Worker bees collect pollen from flowers and carry it in their sacs, or leg baskets. These sacs are rows of small spines on their rear legs. A single bee can collect balls of pollen as large as 0.25 in.

[6.3 mm] in diameter. The pollen is mixed with the bees' saliva to make a substance called bee-bread, used for food.

Nectar is also collected by the workers. They carry it in a special stomach in their bodies called the crop or honey sac. A bee must visit about one thousand flowers to fill its honey sac. It takes 60 full honey sacs to provide enough honey to fill a thimble. Honey is deposited in the honeycomb to ripen and thicken before each cell of the comb is sealed.

Workers use propolis, a resin from trees, to block up holes in their hives. They also use it to seal off the bodies of small animals who get into the hive and are stung to death.

Water is collected by the workers to dilute honey that has become too thick. It is also used to keep the hive moist and cool in hot weather.

Workers that are hatched in the spring or summer live from four to six weeks. Those that hatch in the fall live until the following spring.

The queen bee is nearly twice as large as the other bees. She usually lives from four to five years. Her function is to produce eggs so that the colony can continue. She may lay up to three thousand eggs in one day. When a queen dies, the workers prepare queen cells for the last eggs that were laid. These cells are larger than other cells and are oblong rather than six-sided. Sometimes they are made while a queen is still alive. Eggs are placed in the queen cells, and they hatch into larvae. The larvae are fed royal jelly for a longer period than the usual three days. This makes them develop into queen bees rather than into worker bees. When a queen comes out of her cell, she immediately seeks out and kills any other queen larvae in the hive. Should there be another adult queen present, the two will fight until one of them kills the other. A queen bee never stings any bee except another queen. If she is prevented from killing a rival queen, one of them will leave the hive. She takes two thousand to twenty thousand bees along with her to start a new colony.

Drones are male bees born from unfertilized eggs laid by female workers (see PARTHENOGENESIS). Drones are larger than workers but smaller than queens. Drones do not have stingers. Their tongues are not long enough for them to obtain nectar. That is why they must be fed by the workers.

The main function of the drones is to mate with the queen so that she can lay fertilized eggs. The queen and a drone fly out of the hive and mate in the air.

During the summer, about one hundred drones are permitted to live in the hive and be fed. If other drones appear, they are killed. When food becomes scarce in the fall, the drones in the colony are stung to death and removed from the hive.

BEECH FAMILY The beech family has about five hundred species of trees, including the chestnut and oak. These trees grow to a height of 120 ft. [36.5 m]. Beeches are monoecious, which means that both male and female flowers grow on the same plant. The rounded male flowers are on thin stalks. The female flowers grow in pairs or in groups of three.

Beeches are deciduous, shedding their thin leaves once every year (see DECIDUOUS TREE). The leaves are sometimes colored red or purple. The fruit of these trees, called mast, is an important food for animals. Beechwood is used for furniture, flooring, fuel, and as pulp in making paper.

BEECH
A beech tree growing alone has wide, spreading branches. The small nutlike fruits provide food for squirrels and various rodents.